# Science

**GRADE**

# 4

# Contents

# Introduction

Steck-Vaughn's *Core Skills Science* series offers parents and educators high-quality, curriculum-based products that align with the Common Core Standards for Reading in the Sciences for grades 1–6. The *Core Skills Science* books provide informative and grade-appropriate readings on a wide variety of topics in life, earth, and physical science. Two pages of worksheets follow each reading passage. The book includes:

- clear illustrations, making scientific concepts accessible to young learners

- engaging reading passages, covering a wide variety of topics in life, earth, and physical science

- logically sequenced activities, transitioning smoothly from basic comprehension to higher-order thinking skills

- comprehension questions, ascertaining that students understand what they have read

- vocabulary activities, challenging students to show their understanding of scientific terms

- critical thinking activities, increasing students' ability to analyze, synthesize, and evaluate scientific information

- questions in standardized-test format, helping prepare students for state exams

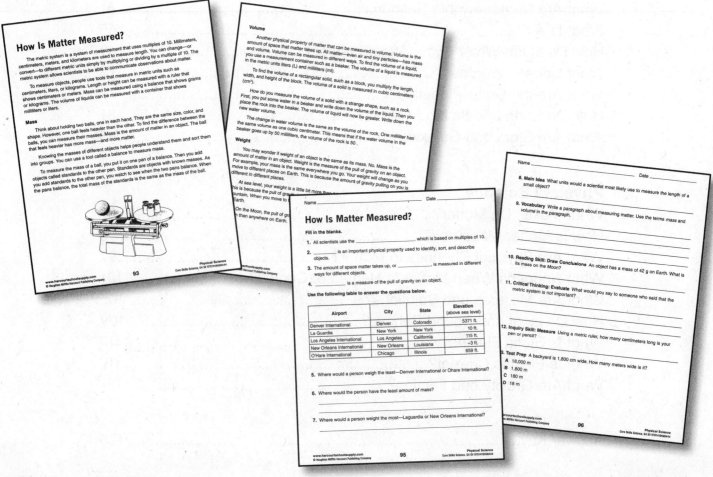

# How Are Living Things Organized?

What is the difference between a live duck and a duck made of bronze? A live duck can carry out life processes. A bronze duck cannot. A life process is something a living thing does to stay alive and make more of its own kind.

All living things carry out life processes. One of these is to eat, or take in nutrients. Nutrients are materials used by living things to grow. Another life process is to reproduce. To reproduce means to make more living things of their own kind.

## Plant and Animal Cells

A cell is the basic building block of all living things. Cells are very tiny. You need a microscope to see them. All cells have parts. Some parts are the same in both plant cells and animal cells. Some are different. For example, plant cells have stiff cell walls. Plant cells also have chloroplasts where the plant makes food.

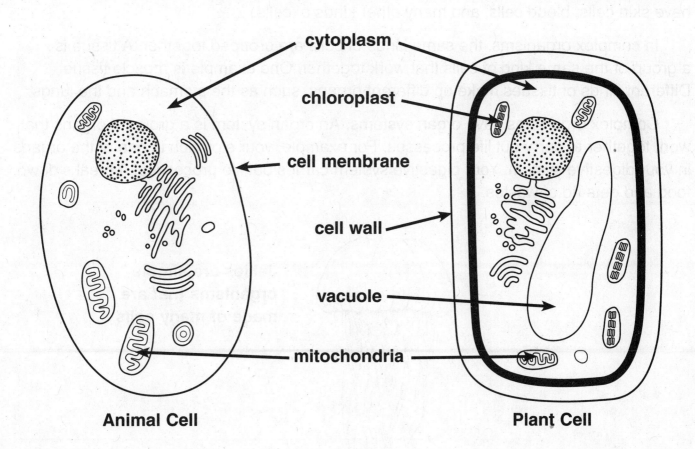

cytoplasm

chloroplast

cell membrane

cell wall

vacuole

mitochondria

**Animal Cell**

**Plant Cell**

## Simple Organisms

An organism is any living thing that can carry out life processes on its own. Some organisms are simple. Some are complex.

**Single Cells**  Some simple organisms are just one single cell. These single cells still carry out life processes. Algae are single-celled organisms. Algae have chloroplasts and can make their own food. Algae give off oxygen as a waste product. Algae make much of the oxygen on Earth.

**Many Cells**  Most of the organisms you know have more than once cell. Your own body contains billions of cells. But some many-celled organisms are much simpler. Jellies have many cells, but have very simple bodies. They do not have organs like you do. An organ is a special part of an organism that does a certain job. Your heart is one of your organs. So is your brain. Jellies do not have hearts, brains, or other organs.

## Complex Organisms

There are many different kinds of cells in complex organisms. For example, you have skin cells, blood cells, and many other kinds of cells.

In complex organisms, the same kinds of cells are grouped together. A tissue is a group of the same kind of cells that work together. One example is muscle tissue. Different kinds of tissues make up different organs, such as the stomach and the lungs.

Complex organisms have organ systems. An organ system is a group of organs that work together to carry out life processes. For example, your stomach is one of the organs in your digestive system. Your digestive system carries out life processes. It breaks down food and gets rid of wastes.

**Jellies are simple organisms that are made of many cells**

Core Skills Science, G4 SV 9781419098444

Name _____    Date _____

# How Are Living Things Organized?

**Label the parts of the plant cell on the diagram below.**

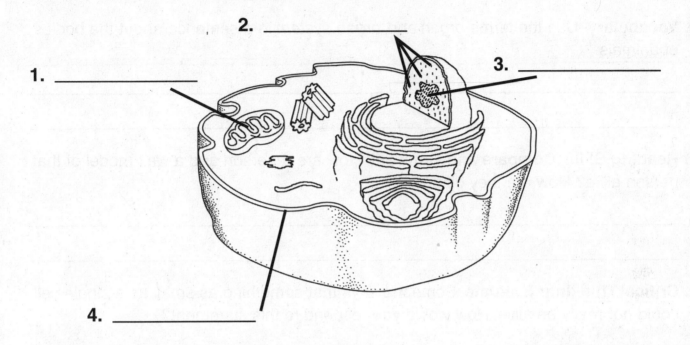

2. _____

1. _____

3. _____

4. _____

**Circle the letter that best answers the question or completes the sentence.**

5. Which could be a simple organism?

   **A.** single cell        **C.** organ systems

   **B.** tissue             **D.** organs

6. Tissue consists of many

   **A.** kinds of organs.       **C.** similar cells.

   **B.** simple organisms.      **D.** organ systems.

7. Both simple organisms and complex organisms

   **A.** are single-celled animals.    **C.** consist of organs.

   **B.** have tissue.                  **D.** perform life processes.

8. Complex organisms are made of cells, tissue, organs, and

   **A.** organ systems.    **C.** life processes.

   **B.** jellies.          **D.** algae.

**Life Science**
Core Skills Science, G4 SV 9781419098444

**9. Main Idea** How are all living things alike?

_____

_____

**10. Vocabulary** Use the terms *organ* and *organ system* in a sentence about the bodies of animals.

_____

_____

**11. Reading Skill: Compare and Contrast** How are a person and a wax model of that person alike? How are they different?

_____

_____

**12. Critical Thinking: Evaluate** Someone says that something as small as a single cell could not really be alive. How would you respond to this statement?

_____

_____

**13. Inquiry Skill: Ask Questions** Pose a question about simple and complex organisms. Use the Internet or library to find the answer.

_____

_____

**14. Test Prep** A gas that plants give off as waste is

   **A** water.

   **B** soil.

   **C** oxygen.

   **D** nutrients.

# How Do Plants Carry Out Life Processes?

Plants are living things. They are made of cells. They carry out life processes. One thing makes most plants different from animals. Plants have special parts to make their own food. They have special parts to carry out other life processes.

The main parts of a plant are the roots, the stem, and the leaves. The root takes in water and materials from the ground. The stem carries water and materials to and from the roots and leaves. A leaf uses sunlight and air to help the plant make food. The parts work together to carry out life processes.

## Comparing Plant Parts

Plants can be sorted into groups. When scientists sort things into groups, they are classifying them. Plants can be classified by their parts. For example, plants with the same kinds of leaves or roots can be grouped together.

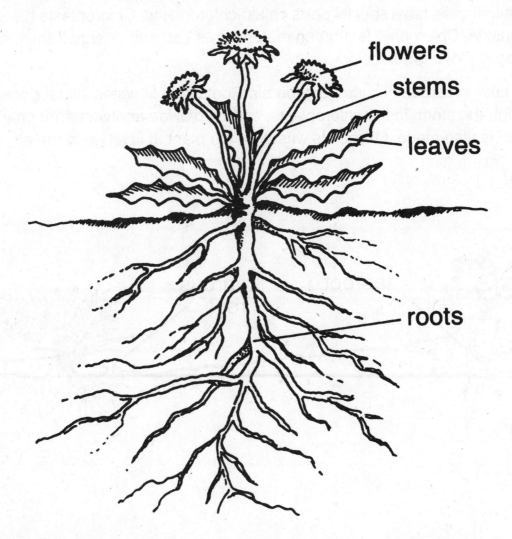

flowers

stems

leaves

roots

Core Skills Science, G4 SV 9781419098444

Some plants have thick leaves. Some plants have broad leaves. Some plants have needle-like leaves. Thick leaves help the plant store water. Needle like leaves help a plant live where it is cold and dry.

Plants can be grouped by the kinds of roots they have. Some plants have one large, main root called a taproot. Others have roots that branch out. These roots are called fibrous roots. Fibrous roots can gather water from a wide area.

Plants have different kinds of stems. Some stems are woody, like tree trunks. Plants with woody stems can survive cold weather. Other plants have soft stems. Plants with soft stems usually cannot survive cold weather.

Some plants have very thick stems, such as cactuses. Thick stems help store water. This helps cactuses survive long periods without rain.

## How Plants Make Food

The way plants make food is called photosynthesis. This often takes place in a plant's leaves. Most leaf cells have special parts called chloroplasts. Chloroplasts have chlorophyll inside. Chlorophyll is a green material that can trap energy from sunlight. It also gives leaves their green color.

Leaves take in carbon dioxide from the air. Roots take in water. Water goes to the leaves through the stem. In the chloroplasts, carbon dioxide and water are changed into food. Oxygen is also made. Oxygen is waste for the plant. It is let go in the air.

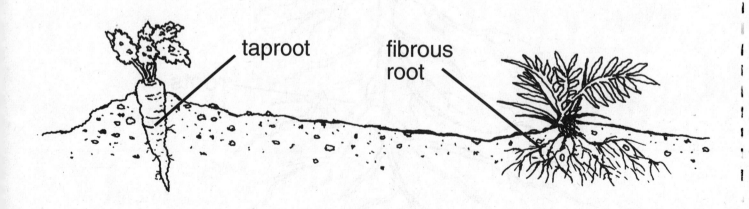

taproot          fibrous root

Name _____     Date _____

# How Do Plants Carry Out Life Processes?

**Label each part of the plant on the diagram below.**

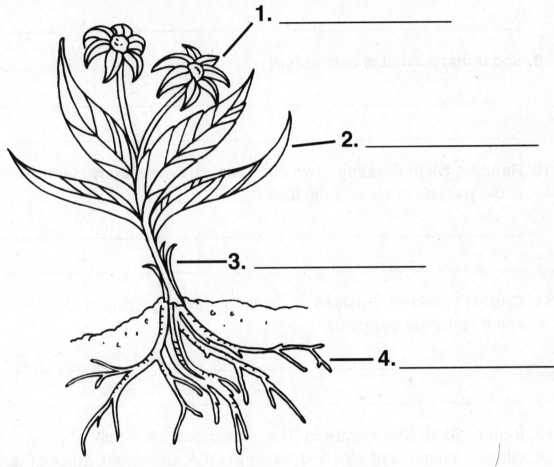

1. _____

2. _____

3. _____

4. _____

**Write answers to the questions on the lines below.**

**5.** What are three ways that plants can be classified?

_____

_____

**6.** What are the two types of root systems?

_____

_____

**7.** What is photosynthesis?

_____

Name _____  Date _____

8. **Main Idea** How do roots help plants meet their needs?

_____

_____

_____

9. **Vocabulary** What is *chlorophyll*?

_____

_____

10. **Reading Skill: Classify** Two bushes each have woody stems. What other features could you use to classify the bushes?

_____

_____

11. **Critical Thinking: Analyze** If a plant does not get any sunlight, which life process can it no longer carry out?

_____

_____

12. **Inquiry Skill: Use Numbers** The data shows the height of bean plants given different amounts of light and water: Plant A, extra light, 10 cm; Plant B, extra water, 7 cm; Plant C, normal light and water, 6 cm. Which factor affected plant growth the most?

_____

_____

13. **Test Prep** What do stems NOT do?

    **A** carry seeds

    **B** carry water

    **C** carry food

    **D** carry nutrients

# What Is the Digestive System?

Your body is made of many, many cells. The same kind of cells make up tissues. Tissues make up organs. Groups of organs make up organ systems. Your stomach and some other organs make up your digestive system.

Each part of your body has a job to do. Each part needs energy and materials to do its job. Food has the energy and materials that the body needs. The digestive system breaks down food so that the body can use it. This is called digestion.

When you eat, your digestive system goes to work. Its job is to break down food into nutrients. Cells use nutrients for energy and growth. The body also uses nutrients to heal cuts and grow new cells.

## The Path of Food

Digestion starts as soon as food enters your mouth and you start chewing. Your teeth grind up food into smaller pieces so that it can travel through your digestive system easier. Your tongue pushes the food around in your mouth and mixes it with saliva.

Saliva is the watery liquid in the mouth. It moistens the food and begins to break it down. Saliva is produced by salivary glands that are located near the back and bottom area of your mouth. Saliva contains chemicals called enzymes. There are hundreds of different enzymes in your body.

The enzymes in saliva change starch in bread into sugar. If you chew a salty cracker for a long time, you will notice that the cracker loses its salty taste and begins to taste sweet. Sugars and starches are both kinds of carbohydrates. Carbohydrates are one of the main nutrients that your body needs.

When you swallow food, it moves into the esophagus. The esophagus is a tube that pushes food to the stomach. The stomach is one of the body's organs. It squeezes food and mixes it with digestive juices. The digestive juices contain enzymes and an acid. The acid is very strong and breaks down food into a soupy mix. Proteins start to digest in the stomach. Food stays in the stomach for one to three hours.

## Completing Digestion

When food leaves the stomach, it goes to the small intestine. The small intestine is the long organ where most digestion takes place. It is curled up inside the body. Food stays in the small intestine from one to six hours. Proteins finish digesting in the small intestine.

The pancreas and the liver are two more organs that help in digestion. Liquids from these two organs are in the small intestine. The liquids help to digest fats and carbohydrates. Nutrients pass from the small intestine into the blood. Blood carries the nutrients to every cell in the body.

Your body does not use all the food you eat. Food that is not digested enters the large intestine. The large intestine is the organ where water and minerals are taken out of the remaining food. Food stays in the large intestine from 12 to 36 hours. What is left over leaves the body as solid waste.

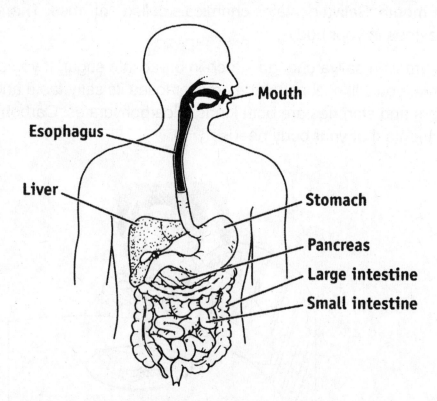

**The Digestive System**

# What Is the Digestive System?

**Complete each sentence using a word or phrase from the box.**

| | | |
|---|---|---|
| **blood** | **energy** | **esophagus** |
| **growth** | **proteins** | **saliva** |
| **small intestine** | **solid waste** | **stomach** |

1. All parts of your body need _____ and other supplies to function properly.

2. Living cells use nutrients for energy, _____, and repair.

3. The main kinds of nutrients your body needs are carbohydrates, _____, vitamins and minerals, and fats.

4. The _____ in your mouth moistens the food and begins to break it down.

5. After swallowing, chewed food moves into the _____, a muscular tube that pushes food toward the stomach.

6. The _____ is a muscular organ that mixes food with digestive juices that contain enzymes and an acid.

7. In the _____, liquids from the pancreas and liver help to digest fats and carbohydrates.

8. Nutrients pass through the walls of the small intestine into the _____, which carries the nutrients and oxygen to every cell in the body.

9. Undigested food that is left over leaves the body as _____.

**10. Main Idea** How does the digestive system help you use the nutrients in food?

_____

**11. Vocabulary** Use the term *large intestine* in a sentence about digestion.

_____

_____

**12. Reading Skill: Main Idea and Details** What happens to food in the small intestine?

_____

_____

**13. Critical Thinking: Analyze** Make a flow chart to show the path of food through the digestive system.

**14. Test Prep** Saliva comes from _____ in your mouth.

   **A** teeth

   **B** glands

   **C** stomach

   **D** organs

# What Are the Circulatory and Respiratory Systems?

Living things need the oxygen in air. The respiratory system brings oxygen into the body and gets rid of wastes. The circulatory system carries oxygen to the cells and carries away wastes.

## The Respiratory System

As you breathe, you take air into the body and push it back out. Body parts that help you breathe make up the respiratory system.

When you inhale, you breathe in. When you exhale, you breathe out. The diaphragm is a muscle that helps you breathe. It moves down as you inhale. It moves up as you exhale.

When you inhale, you take air into your nose or mouth. The air moves into the trachea. The trachea is a tube that connects the throat and lungs. The lungs are the main organs of the respiratory system.

Millions of tiny air sacs are in the lungs. In the air sacs, oxygen moves from the air to the blood. Blood carries oxygen to all your cells. Carbon dioxide moves from the blood to the air. When you breathe out, your body gets rid of carbon dioxide.

## The Circulatory System

Blood brings oxygen to the cells. It takes away carbon dioxide. Blood also carries wnutrients and water to the cells. The job of the circulatory system is to carry oxygen, nutrients, water, and wastes.

Blood flows through blood vessels. You can think of blood vessels as pipes. The heart is a pump. It pumps the blood through the pipes.

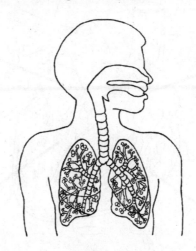

The respiratory and circulatory systems work together. The blood picks up oxygen from the lungs. The blood then flows into the heart. The heart pumps the blood through arteries. An artery is a blood vessel that carries blood away from the heart. The blood goes through the arteries to capillaries.

A capillary is a tiny blood vessel. It passes oxygen to the cells. It connects an artery to a vein. A vein carries blood back to the heart. The blood enters the heart and gets pumped to the lungs. In the lungs the blood picks up more oxygen.

Oxygen, nutrients, and water pass from the blood to the cells in the capillaries. Wastes pass from the cells to the blood in the capillaries.

Blood has solid parts and a liquid part. The liquid part is called plasma. The plasma carries nutrients and water to the cells. The solid parts of blood include red blood cells, white blood cells, and platelets.

Red blood cells are round. They pick up oxygen from the lungs. They carry oxygen to the cells of the body. White blood cells are larger than red blood cells. They help the body fight disease. Platelets are small. They help to heal cuts.

## The Heart

The heart is a pump. It is made of muscle. The heart pumps blood all day and all night. Inside the heart are four spaces. The spaces are called chambers. The top two are the atriums. Blood from veins enters the heart through the atriums.

The bottom two chambers are the ventricles. The ventricles are the pumping chambers. They pump the blood to the lungs or to the body. They push the blood out of the heart into the arteries. You can feel the pumping of the blood as your pulse. Press your fingers against an artery in your wrist to feel your pulse.

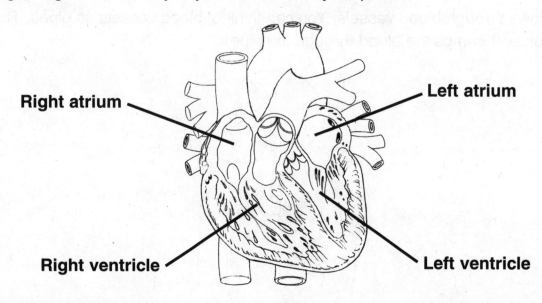

Right atrium

Left atrium

Right ventricle

Left ventricle

Name _____ Date _____

# What Are the Circulatory and Respiratory Systems?

**Fill in the blanks.**

1. _____ are solid parts of the blood that help heal cuts.

2. When you exhale, or breathe out, your body gets rid of _____ as waste.

3. The _____ is a dome-shaped muscle that helps you to breathe.

4. A _____ is a tiny blood vessel.

**Complete the diagram below.**

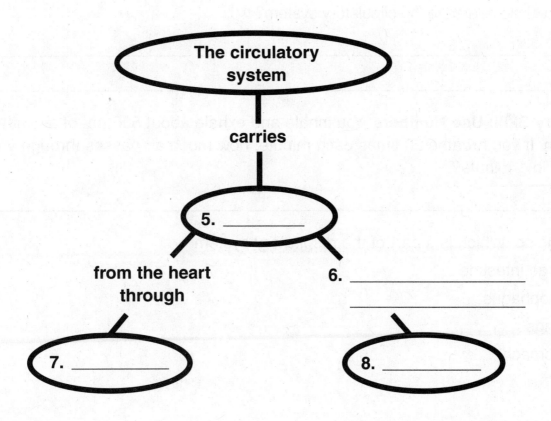

The circulatory system

carries

5. _____

from the heart through

6. _____
   _____

7. _____

8. _____

9. **Main Idea** How do the respiratory and circulatory systems work together in the body?

_____

_____

10. **Vocabulary** Use the term *heart* in a sentence about the circulatory system.

_____

_____

11. **Reading Skill: Compare and Contrast** How are red blood cells and white blood cells alike? How are they different?

_____

_____

12. **Critical Thinking: Evaluate** The words *circle* and *circulatory* sound similar. How do you think a circle relates to the circulatory system?

_____

_____

13. **Inquiry Skill: Use Numbers** You inhale and exhale about 500 mL of air with each breath. If you breathe 20 times each minute, how much air passes through your lungs in 1 minute?

_____

14. **Test Prep** Which is a part of the respiratory system?

   **A** large intestine

   **B** esophagus

   **C** lungs

   **D** stomach

# What Are the Skeletal and Muscular Systems?

The skeletal and muscular systems protect the body. They support the body and allow it to move.

## The Skeletal System

The skeletal system, or skeleton, does three important jobs. First, it gives the body shape and support. Second, it protects the organs inside your body. Third, it works with the muscles to move the body. The skeleton is made of bone.

Most animals have a skeleton. However, insects have an exoskeleton. An exoskeleton is a hard covering outside the body. An exoskeleton gives an insect shape and support. It also protects the insect.

The adult human skeleton has 206 bones. Your spine is a column of small bones. It runs down your back. The spine is also called a backbone. The ribs are attached to the spine. They protect the heart and lungs. Your skull is the bony part of your head. It protects your brain.

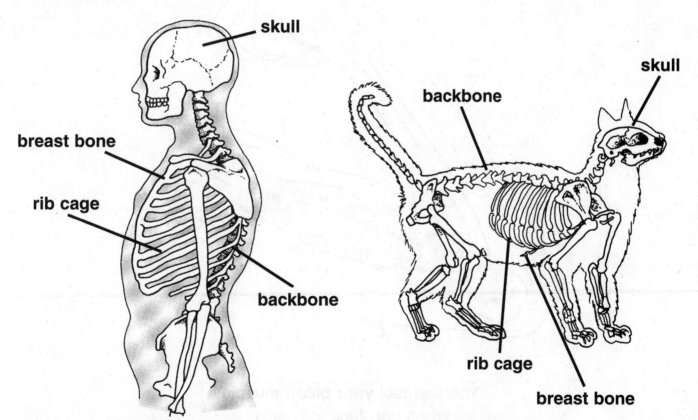

**Humans and some animals have similar bone structures.**

You have long bones in your arms and legs. These bones help the body move. Bones come together at joints. Soft tissue connects bones and holds a joint together. Joints work in different ways. Your knee is a joint that moves back and forth like a hinge. Your shoulder is a joint that allows movement in many directions. It is called a ball-and-socket joint.

## The Muscular System

The muscular system is made of muscle. Muscle is tissue that makes body parts move. There are three kinds of muscle: skeletal, cardiac, and smooth muscle.

Skeletal muscle moves your bones. Skeletal muscles move when you think about them. Muscles that move when you think about them are called voluntary muscles.

Cardiac muscle is found only in the heart. Smooth muscle is found in blood vessels and many organs. Cardiac and smooth muscles move without you thinking about them. They are called involuntary muscles.

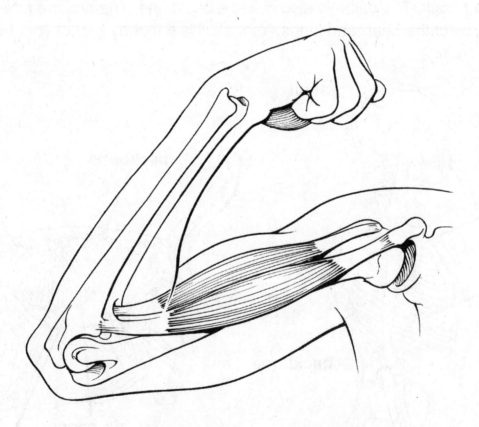

**You can feel your bicep muscle
when you flex your arm.**

Name _____ Date _____

# What Are the Skeletal and Muscular Systems?

**Complete each sentence using a word or phrase from the box.**

| | | |
|---|---|---|
| ball-and-socket joint | cartilage | hinge |
| ribs | skull | spine |

1. _____ form a cage of curved bones attached to the spine that protects the lungs and heart

2. The hip is a _____.

3. _____ cushions most bones where they meet.

4. The bony part of the head that protects the brain is the _____.

5. The _____ is a column of small bones that runs down the back and keeps it straight.

6. The knee is a joint that works like a _____.

**Write the answer to each question.**

7. What are the three kinds of muscle?

_____

_____

8. Which muscles are voluntary and which are involuntary?

_____

_____

**9. Main Idea** What is the job of the skeletal system?

_____

_____

**10. Vocabulary** Use the term *muscular system* in a sentence about the heart.

_____

_____

**11. Critical Thinking: Evaluate** What would happen if your body had no skeletal muscles?

_____

_____

_____

**12. Inquiry Skill: Use Models** How could you make a model of a ball-and-socket joint?

_____

_____

_____

**13. Test Prep** A hard covering outside the body is called the

   **A** muscle.

   **B** tissue.

   **C** exoskeleton.

   **D** spine.

# How Do Plant and Animal Life Cycles Vary?

A small seed is planted in the ground. The seed grows into a tall tree. The tree flowers and makes its own seeds. One day the tree dies. This is the life cycle of a tree.

A life cycle is the series of changes that happen during a lifetime. The changes in a life cycle include birth, becoming an adult, reproduction, and death. Flowering plants grow flowers during their life cycles. Flowers make seeds that will grow into new plants.

The stamen of a flower makes pollen. Flowers make seeds when pollen is moved from the stamens to the pistil. Wind, water, and animals can move pollen. Each seed holds an embryo. An embryo is a plant or animal in the earliest stages of development.

Some seeds will fall in places where they can germinate. To germinate means to begin growing a new plant.

## Life Spans of Plants

A life span is the length of time it takes a living thing to complete its life cycle. The length of a life span is different for different kinds of plants. Bean seeds will grow into plants, make seeds, and die in one summer. A maple tree may live for hundreds of years.

## Life Spans and Life Cycles of Animals

Different kinds of animals have different life spans. Smaller animals usually have shorter life spans than larger animals of the same kind. For example, lizards and alligators are both reptiles. A small lizard may live only 2 years, but an alligator can live 60 years. This is not always true, however.

**life span: 2 years**

**life span: 60 years**

Many animals lay eggs during their life cycles. For example, baby birds hatch from eggs. The babies grow and become adults. To reproduce, adult female birds lay eggs. In time, the adult birds die.

Rabbits, bears, and humans are mammals. Mammals do not lay eggs. Their young are born live. Like baby birds, young mammals grow and become adults. The adults reproduce and in time die.

## Metamorphosis

How are alligators and birds alike? How are alligators and insects alike? Alligators, birds, and insects do not look the same, but they are all animals. They also all lay eggs. An egg is the first stage in the life cycle of most animals.

All reptiles lay eggs. All birds and most fish and amphibians lay eggs. Even insects lay eggs.

Different types of animals lay different numbers of eggs. An eagle may lay 2 or 3 eggs at a time. An ocean sunfish can lay around 300 million eggs at one time.

Offspring hatch from eggs. An offspring is a new living thing born when parents reproduce. An offspring grows into an adult.

Some living things change form in different stages of their life cycles. This process of change is called metamorphosis. Many insects change form four times. This is called complete metamorphosis.

The egg is the first stage. The egg hatches into a wormlike form called a larva. The larva is the second stage. The larva eats and grows larger. In the third stage, the larva forms a hard shell around itself. This is called the pupa. In the fourth stage, the adult insect comes out of the pupa. The insect looks very different at each stage.

Some insects change form only three times. This is called incomplete metamorphosis. The egg is the first stage. The nymph is the second stage. The nymph looks like the adult without wings. The nymph will get bigger, grow wings, and become an adult. The adult is the third stage.

# How Do Plant and Animal Life Cycles Vary?

**Use the diagram below to answer the questions.**

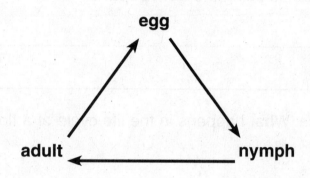

1. Does this diagram show complete or incomplete metamorphosis? Explain.

   _____

   _____

   _____

2. Does this diagram show the life cycle of a bird, an alligator, or an insect? Explain.

   _____

   _____

**Fill in the blanks.**

3. A plant or animal in the earliest stages of development is called a(n)
   _____.

4. Some plant seeds land in places where they can _____, or begin growing into a new plant.

5. The wormlike form that hatches from an egg is called a(n) _____.

**6. Main Idea** What are the main stages in the life cycle of flowering plant?

_____

_____

**7. Vocabulary** Write a sentence using the term *pupa*.

_____

_____

**8. Reading Skill: Sequence** What happens in the life cycle of a flowering plant after it grows flowers?

_____

**9. Critical Thinking: Apply** What questions would you ask in an interview of a scientist who studies fruit flies?

_____

_____

**10. Inquiry Skill: Record Data** Make a bar graph to record the following data. Title your bar graph *Life Spans of Different Snakes*. Garter snake, 8 years; Indigo snake, 17 years; Boa constrictor, 23 years; Anaconda, 30 years. Research how big each snake is.

**11. Test Prep:** The stamen of a flower

  **A** protects the seed.

  **B** holds the embryo.

  **C** is part of the pistil.

  **D** produces pollen.

# What Are the Parts of Ecosystems?

Plants and animals are living things. To live and grow, plants and animals need nonliving things. Nonliving things include water, air and light. An ecosystem is made up of all the living and nonliving things that interact in an area.

Soil is a nonliving thing. Plants grow in soil. Soil is made up of tiny pieces of rock and organic matter. Organic matter is the remains of plants and animals. It is rich in nutrients. Nutrients are materials that help living things grow.

Both plants and animals need sunlight. Plants need sunlight to make food. Some plants and animals can live only where it is warm. Others grow better in the shade of trees.

## Different Ecosystems

Each ecosystem is different. The nonliving parts of each are different. Only some living things can only live where its needs are met.

**A Polar Ecosystem** There is no soil in a polar ecosystem. There is only ice. Temperatures are very cold. There is little or no sunlight for about half the year. Some animals do live in a polar ecosystem. Polar bears have thick fur to keep warm. The bears hunt and eat animals that live in the ocean water.

**A Desert Ecosystem** It is very hot during the day in a desert ecosystem. There is very little rain in a desert. The soil has few nutrients. Some plants and animals do live in a desert. Desert plants send roots deep into the ground to find water. Desert animals look for food at night when it is cooler.

## Communities and Populations

A forest ecosystem has many kinds of living things. Many kinds of plants and animals can find the things they need to live in a forest.

A living thing can live only in an environment that meets its needs. An environment is everything that surrounds and affects a living thing.

All the living things in an ecosystem make up a community. A community is made up of different populations of living things. A population is all the members of one kind of plant or animal. For example, all the beavers in a forest are one population.

## The Right Ecosystem

In a rainforest, it rains a lot. Many rainforests are warm all year. There is a rainforest in Washington State. The temperatures of this rainforest are mild. Trees grow close together. This rainforest provides shelter and water for many kinds of animals.

A prairie is a grassy area with few or no trees. Prairies get more rain than deserts, but less than forests. Winters are cold, and summers are hot. The prairie is home to animals that eat grasses and their seeds.

There are ecosystems in cities. New York City's Central Park is home for many plants and animals. New York City is in a temperate zone. A temperate zone is an area that rarely gets very hot or very cold.

The Florida Everglades is an ecosystem. Most of the land is covered by water. Some trees and tall grasses grow from the muddy water. Water plants and animals such as shrimp and fish live in the water.

Conditions vary in different parts of each ecosystem. Plants and animals live where the conditions are right for them.

Name _____ Date _____

# What Are the Parts of Ecosystems?

**Circle the letter that best answers the question or completes the sentence.**

1. What makes up an ecosystem?

   **A** living and nonliving things
   **B** air and nutrients
   **C** water
   **D** sand and rocks

2. What does shade provide for animals?

   **A** protection
   **B** hot temperatures
   **C** sunlight
   **D** nutrients

3. A living thing will survive

   **A** only in the desert.
   **B** only in the shade.
   **C** only where its needs are met.
   **D** only in a polar ecosystem.

4. Polar ecosystems have no

   **A** animals.
   **B** soil.
   **C** water.
   **D** ice.

**Write answers to the questions on the lines below.**

5. What is a community?

   _____

   _____

6. What is a population?

   _____

   _____

7. What is a prairie?

   _____

   _____

**8. Main Idea** How do living things in an ecosystem interact?

_____

_____

**9. Vocabulary** Use the term *organic matter* in a sentence about soil.

_____

_____

**10. Reading Skill: Cause and Effect** What might happen if all the trees in a forest ecosystem were cut down?

_____

_____

**11. Critical Thinking: Analyze** What is the relationship between living and nonliving parts of an ecosystem?

_____

_____

**12. Inquiry Skill: Research** Use resource materials to research a rainforest ecosystem. Why do so few plants grow on the rainforest floor?

_____

_____

**13. Test Prep** The nonliving parts of an ecosystem

   **A** are the same in every ecosystem.

   **B** determine which plants and animals can live in the ecosystem.

   **C** include animals and plants

   **D** do not interact with the living parts of an ecosystem.

# How Does Energy Flow in a Food Web?

All living things need energy to stay alive. They get that energy from food. Plants are producers. Producers are living things that make their own food. The way most plants make food is called photosynthesis. This takes place in a plant's leaves. Light energy from the Sun is trapped inside the leaves. Plants use light energy and carbon dioxide gas from the air to make food.

## Predator and Prey

Animals are consumers. Consumers are living things that eat other living things. Some animals eat plants. Some animals eat other animals. A predator is an animal that hunts other animals for food. Prey is an animal that is hunted for food by another animal.

A consumer, such as a rabbit, eats a plant. The rabbit receives some of the plant's energy. A predator, such as an owl, eats the rabbit. The owl receives a smaller amount of the plant's energy. Energy flows from the Sun to a producer, and then to consumers.

## Food Chains

A food chain shows the path of food energy in an ecosystem. Remember that an ecosystem is all living and nonliving things that interact in one place. A food chain begins with producers.

Consumers are also part of the food chain. There are three kinds of consumers. An herbivore is an animal that eats only plants. An omnivore is an animal that eats both plants and animals. A carnivore is an animal that only eats other animals.

For example, a plant makes its own food. An herbivore, such as a vole, eats the plant. An omnivore, such as a skunk, eats the vole. Finally, a carnivore, such as an owl, eats the skunk.

At each step in the food chain, some of the energy is lost. For example, the plant does not keep all of the food it makes. It uses some energy to grow flowers and seeds for the plant.

The vole gets only some of the plant's energy. The vole uses some of that energy to run from its predators. The skunk gets less energy from eating the vole. There is less energy available at each step in a food chain. That is why most food chains only have four or five steps.

## Food Webs

Most ecosystems have many different kinds of plants and animals. Each plant or animal is part of more than one food chain. A food web shows how one plant or animal is part of another food chain.

Look at the food web. The plants, ground squirrel, and fox are part of a food chain. Ground squirrels eat plants. Foxes eat ground squirrels. However the ground squirrel is prey for the hawk, too. The ground squirrel is part of another food chain.

Some animals eat many kinds of plants for energy. Some animals eat many kinds of animals for energy. Some animals fight each other for the same kind of food.

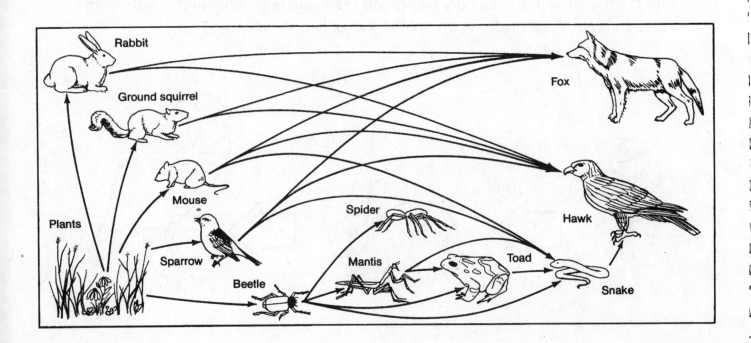

# How Does Energy Flow in a Food Web?

**Write answers to the questions on the lines below. Use the diagram below.**

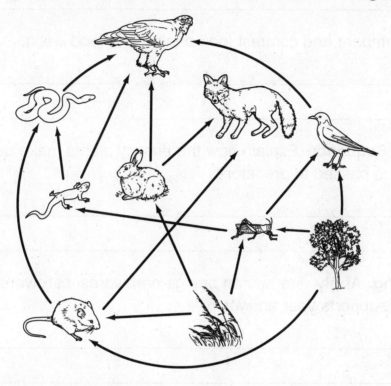

**1.** Why is the drawing an example of a food chain? Explain.

_____

**2.** Is the bird, the fox, or the rabbit an omnivore? Explain.

_____

**3.** Which two predators eat the lizard?

_____

**4.** Which animals are herbivores?

_____

**5.** Which two animals are predators but never prey?

_____

**6. Main Idea** Describe the flow of energy in a food web.

_____

_____

**7. Vocabulary** Compare and contrast food chains and food webs.

_____

_____

_____

**8. Reading Skill: Sequence** Explain how the energy plants make during photosynthesis is passed to predators.

_____

_____

_____

**9. Critical Thinking: Apply** Are human beings herbivores, carnivores, or omnivores? What evidence supports your answer?

_____

_____

_____

**10. Inquiry Skill: Use Models** Draw a food chain that includes yourself.

**11. Test Prep** An animal that is eaten by another animal is a(n)

   **A** predator.            **C** carnivore.

   **B** prey.              **D** omnivore.

# How Is Matter Cycled in an Ecosystem?

Predators spend much of their time hunting for prey. However, some animals look for dead animals. These animals are scavengers. A scavenger is an animal that eats the remains or wastes of other animals.

Scavengers are consumers. Scavengers get energy from eating the remains of things that were once alive. Scavengers often eat the remains of prey that was killed by another animal.

## Predators and Scavengers

Predators hunt and kill other animals for food. Scavengers eat what the predators do not eat. For example, a predator such as a wolf kills an animal such as a moose. The wolf does not eat all of the moose. Scavengers eat what is left.

Some scavengers are prey for other animals. When a predator eats a scavenger, energy is passed along in the food chain. This is one reason why scavengers are an important part of a food web. Scavengers are a part of every kind of ecosystem.

## Helpful Organisms

Fungi and bacteria are organisms. Some kinds of fungi and bacteria can make people sick. However, most fungi and bacteria are helpful.

**A vulture is a scavenger.**

All organisms die. You know that some dead organisms are eaten by scavengers. But some are not. When some organisms die, their bodies decay, or break down into simpler parts. Fungi and bacteria are decomposers. A decomposer is a living thing that breaks down the remains of dead organisms. All food chains end with decomposers. For example, bacteria and fungi help break down a dead tree. As the tree decays, energy is released into the soil. New living things use this energy to grow.

Organisms decay and release energy for new living things to use. This is called recycling. Recycling is the process of breaking down things into a different form that can be used again. Decay happens much faster in places where it is warm and wet. Animals that die in places where it is cold and dry do not decay for a long time.

Decomposers help the environment. They clean up the remains of dead organisms. They recycle valuable energy that other organisms use to grow. Some decomposers are microorganisms. A microorganism is a tiny living thing that can only be seen with a microscope. Bacteria are one kind of microorganism.

## Benefits to Plants and Animals

Decomposers are a very important part of ecosystems. They release energy that plants and animals need to stay alive. Decomposers clean up dead organisms. Other living things can live where the dead organisms once were.

People can help make a good environment for decomposers. A compost pile is a place set aside for dead organisms to decay. Most people throw away food, paper, dead leaves, and grass. These things are good for composts piles.

Bacteria and fungi live in great numbers in compost piles. These decomposers help the compost pile decay. Energy is put back into the soil as the compost pile decays. New living things can use the energy to grow.

Name _____    Date _____

# How Is Matter Cycled in an Ecosystem?

**Use the diagram below to answer the questions.**

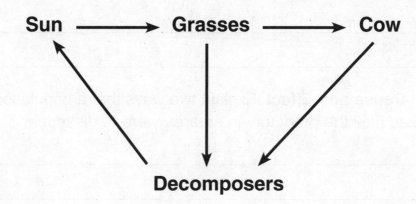

1. What happens to the grass that is not eaten? Explain.

_____

_____

2. What is the beginning of the web? Why?

_____

_____

3. What happens after the cow eats grass?

_____

_____

4. What process is taking place in this disgram?

_____

_____

**5. Main Idea** What two types of organisms get energy from the remains of once-living things?

_____

**6. Vocabulary** Use the term *microorganism* in a sentence.

_____

_____

**7. Reading Skill: Cause and Effect** Explain two ways that a population of scavengers would be affected if all the predators in an area were to disappear.

_____

_____

_____

**8. Critical Thinking: Infer** What would be the effect on an ecosystem if there were no decomposers?

_____

_____

_____

**9. Inquiry Skill: Use Variables** In an experiment, one decaying log is placed in a covered cardboard box and another in a clear box. The temperature and amount of water for each are the same. What is the variable, or the thing that changes, which is being tested?

_____

**10. Test Prep** A living thing that breaks down the remains of dead organisms is a

   **A** prey.

   **B** decomposer.

   **C** predator.

   **D** carnivore.

# How Are Organisms Adapted to Survive?

Different plants and animals live in different environments. The place where a plant or animal lives is called its habitat. The habitat of a dolphin is the ocean. The habitat of a cactus is the desert.

Plants and animals have adaptations. An adaptation can be a physical feature or a behavior that helps a plant or animal survive. The webbed feet of a duck are an adaptation that is a physical feature. Hunting at night is an adaptation that is a behavior.

The role a plant or animal plays in its environment is called its niche. A niche includes the kind of food a living thing uses. An opossum's niche includes eating berries at night. Many living things can share a habitat. However, each has its own niche.

## Camouflage

Some animals hide by looking like what is around them. These animals have an adaptation called camouflage. Camouflage is the coloring or marking of an animal that helps it look like what is around them. Camouflage can help both predators and prey.

The color and spots of a young deer's fur help the deer look like its forest habitat. Predators have a hard time seeing it.

An arctic fox is a predator that uses camouflage. Its fur looks like what is around it. Its prey does not see the fox.

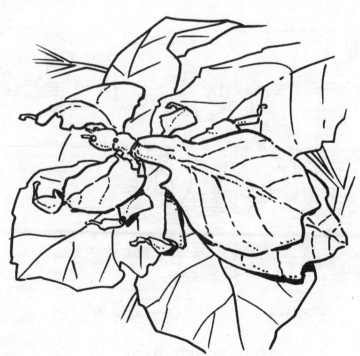

Core Skills Science, G4 SV 9781419098444

## Color and Mimicry

Some animals have bright colors. Other animals can see them easily. This adaptation is called warning coloration. The blue poison dart frog stands out. Its bright color warns predators that it is poisonous.

Some animals protect themselves by using mimicry. Mimicry is an adaptation where an animal looks like another animal or a plant. Many insects use mimicry. The South American owl butterfly has large spots on its wings. The spots look like the eyes of an owl. These spots scare away birds that might eat the butterfly.

## Behavior

Behavior can help a predator as it hunts. Wolves and other animals hunt in groups. The group surrounds the prey so it cannot escape. Behavior also helps prey survive. Rabbits run in a zig-zag pattern. This behavior can help them escape from predators.

Some animals such as bats, frogs, and chipmunks have an adaptation that helps them survive winter. They hibernate, or go into a deep sleep, during which they use very little energy. This behavior helps the animals get through long, cold winters.

**Wolves hunt in groups.**

Name _____  Date _____

# How Are Organisms Adapted To Survive?

**Fill in the blanks using the terms *mimicry*, *camouflage*, and *behavior*.**

1. _____ A kangaroo rat stays in its burrow to avoid the heat.

2. _____ An arctic fox has fur that turns white in winter.

3. _____ A South American owl butterfly has spots that look like an owl's eyes.

4. _____ A rabbit runs in a zig-zag to escape a predator.

5. _____ The color and spots of a young deer help it look like its habitat.

6. _____ An archer fish shoots a jet of water at insects to knock them into the water.

7. _____ Wolves hunt in groups so they can surround their prey.

**Life Science**
Core Skills Science, G4 SV 9781419098444

**8. Main Idea** Explain why it is important for plants and animals to be adapted to their environment.

_____

_____

**9. Vocabulary** What is a niche?

_____

_____

**10. Reading Skill: Problem-Solution** How does hibernation help frogs survive the winter?

_____

_____

**11. Critical Thinking: Apply** Some katydids look like the leaves they live on. What might happen to a katydid in the fall when the leaves change color?

_____

_____

**12. Inquiry Skill: Observe** What features of an insect would you look at to determine what adaptations the insect has?

_____

_____

**13. Test Prep** Hawks are birds that hunt small animals. A hawk would most likely have feet with

   **A** webs.

   **B** large claws.

   **C** small toes.

   **D** no claws.

# What Is the Rock Cycle?

Earth is made up of layers. If you could take a part out of Earth, you would see the layers. The outer layer is the crust. The ocean floor and all the land on Earth are part of the crust. The crust is the thinnest layer of Earth. It is made up of rock. Rock is a solid material made up of one or more minerals. A mineral is a solid material found in Earth's crust that has a definite chemical makeup.

The next layer of Earth is the mantle. The mantle is a thick layer of rock beneath the crust. In the upper part of the mantle, the rock is melted and soft. This is called molten rock. The lower part of the mantle is solid.

In the center of Earth is the core. The core is a ball with two parts. The outer part is liquid, and the inner part is solid. The solid inner part is the hottest part of Earth.

## Rocks of Earth's Crust

Earth's crust is made of three basic kinds of rock. Each kind forms in a different way. Each kind has different features. The first kind of rock is igneous rock. When molten rock from Earth's mantle cools and hardens, it forms igneous rock.

Sometimes molten rock cools slowly inside Earth's crust. Sometimes molten rock flows from an opening in the crust. A volcano is such an opening. This molten rock cools quickly.

There are different types of igneous rock. The molten rock contains different minerals. As the rock cools and hardens, these minerals form crystals. For example, diamond is a crystal.

The second kind of rock is sedimentary rock. Bits of sand, rock, soil, and the remains of once-living things mix together and make sediment. Sedimentary rock forms when sediment hardens.

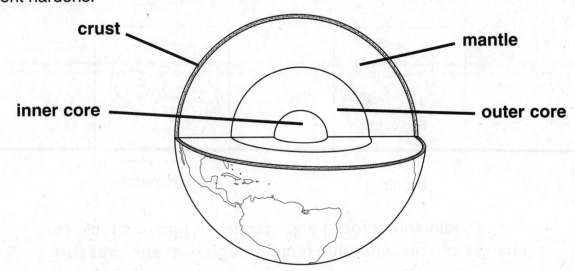

crust    mantle    inner core    outer core

Wind, moving water, and moving ice carry sediment. Then it settles in low places. It slowly packs together. Dissolved minerals fill in any cracks and glue the pieces together. Sedimentary rock is formed.

The third kind of rock is metamorphic rock. Metamorphic rock forms beneath Earth's surface. Metamorphic rock is new rock that forms when existing rocks are changed by heat, pressure, or chemicals.

Igneous and sedimentary rocks can be changed into metamorphic rock. Metamorphic rocks can also be changed to make new metamorphic rock.

## How Rocks Change

Any kind of rock can change into another kind. For example, metamorphic rock can become sedimentary rock. Rocks may seem too hard to break or change, but they do. Wind, moving water, and ice can break rocks into pieces. This is called weathering.

Scientists call the changes rocks go through the rock cycle. The rock cycle never ends. Rocks build up and wear away again and again.

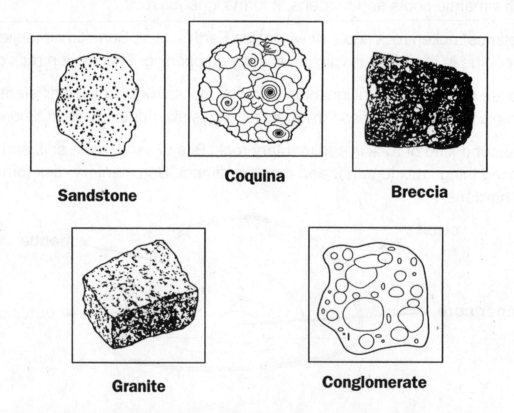

**Sandstone**

**Coquina**

**Breccia**

**Granite**

**Conglomerate**

**These sedimentary rocks and granite, an igneous rock, can change into metamorphic rock through heat and pressure.**

Name _____ Date _____

# What Is the Rock Cycle?

**Fill in the blanks in the diagram below.**

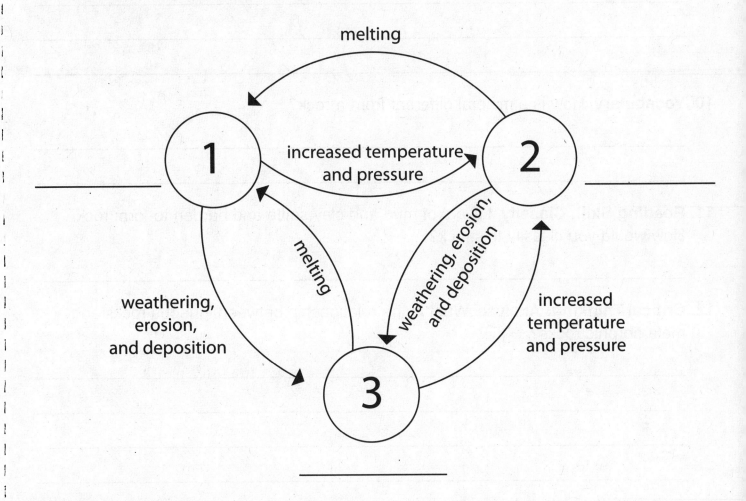

**Fill in the blanks.**

4. As molten rock cools and hardens, the _____ in it form crystals.

5. Breaking rock into sediment is called _____.

6. _____ is carried by wind, moving water, and moving ice.

7. Both igneous and sedimentary rocks can be changed into
   _____ rocks.

8. The _____ is the continuous series of changes that rocks go through.

**9. Main Idea** What are three ways that rocks can change?

_____

_____

_____

_____

**10. Vocabulary** How is a mineral different from a rock?

_____

_____

**11. Reading Skill: Classify** Layers of mud and clay settle and harden to form rock. How would you classify this rock?

_____

**12. Critical Thinking: Analyze** What is the relationship between igneous rocks and metamorphic rocks?

_____

_____

_____

_____

**13. Test Prep** The continents and ocean floor are part of Earth's

   **A** inner core.

   **B** crust.

   **C** mantle.

   **D** outer core.

# What Are Rapid Surface Changes?

Earth's crust seems solid, but it is cracked in some places. A crack in Earth's crust is called a fault. Earthquakes take place along a fault. An earthquake is a sudden movement of part of Earth's crust.

Parts of Earth's crust are moving very slowly. Sometimes the parts of the crust come together, move apart, or slide past each other. When the parts hit each other, it often causes an earthquake.

Earth's crust is always changing. Forces deep inside Earth push on the rock above. This pushing may build up for many years. Sometimes the pushing on the rock becomes too great. Then the parts on either side of a fault may move suddenly. This sudden movement is an earthquake.

The strength of an earthquake relates to the amount of pushing. When the pushing is very great, a strong earthquake takes place. During an earthquake, the movement of the rock can create landforms. Mountains are pushed up. Valleys can form. New faults can form, too.

## Volcanoes

Melted rock from Earth's mantle is called magma. As magma rises, some of it gets hard and becomes igneous rock. Some magma pushes its way through a fault to Earth's surface. It flows onto Earth's surface as lava.

A volcano is an opening in Earth's crust. When a volcano erupts, hot ash, gases, and molten rock escape from deep inside Earth.

Volcanoes can erupt in different ways. Thick slow-moving lava erupts from some volcanoes. Other volcanoes erupt suddenly. They can quickly change Earth's surface.

Mount St. Helens is a volcano in the state of Washington. On May 18, 1980, Mount St. Helens erupted. Ash and hot gases blew through the air. The heat melted the snow on the mountainside. Rocks, soil, mud, and water crashed down. Forests for many miles were completely destroyed!

## Landslides

When Mount St. Helens erupted, it caused a huge mudslide. A landslide is the sudden movement of loose rock and soil down a steep slope. If the soil is soaked with water, the landslide is called a mudslide.

Earthquakes and volcanic eruptions can cause landslides and mudslides. Heavy rains or the sudden melting of snow can cause mudslides. A mudslide can carry away trees, boulders, cars, and even houses.

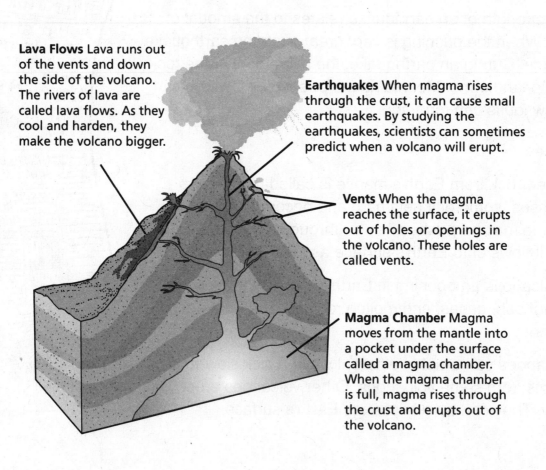

**Lava Flows** Lava runs out of the vents and down the side of the volcano. The rivers of lava are called lava flows. As they cool and harden, they make the volcano bigger.

**Earthquakes** When magma rises through the crust, it can cause small earthquakes. By studying the earthquakes, scientists can sometimes predict when a volcano will erupt.

**Vents** When the magma reaches the surface, it erupts out of holes or openings in the volcano. These holes are called vents.

**Magma Chamber** Magma moves from the mantle into a pocket under the surface called a magma chamber. When the magma chamber is full, magma rises through the crust and erupts out of the volcano.

# What Are Rapid Surface Changes?

**Match each definition to its term.**

**Definitions**

____ 1. a sudden movement in Earth's crust

____ 2. an opening in Earth's crust through which molten rock flows

____ 3. molten rock beneath Earth's surface

____ 4. molten rock that reaches Earth's surface when a volcano erupts

____ 5. a sudden movement of loose rock and soil down a steep slope

**Terms**

**A.** volcano

**B.** landslide

**C.** earthquake

**D.** lava

**E.** magma

**Fill in the blanks.**

6. Earthquakes are commonly caused when _____ come together, move apart, or slide past each other.

7. During an earthquake, the movement of rock near Earth's surface can _____, such as mountains.

8. _____ causes some magma to push its way through faults and flow onto Earth's surface as lava.

9. Volcanoes can quickly _____ Earth's surface.

10. Earthquakes and volcanic eruptions can trigger _____.

**11. Main Idea** What are three ways that Earth's surface can rapidly change?

_____

_____

**12. Vocabulary** Write a sentence using the word *magma*.

_____

_____

_____

**13. Reading Skill: Cause and Effect** Identify three effects that an earthquake may have on the landscape.

_____

_____

_____

**14. Inquiry Skill: Use Models** Describe how you could make a model of a landslide.

_____

_____

_____

_____

**15. Test Prep** A mudslide is LEAST likely to occur

   **A** on a steep hillside.

   **B** early in the spring.

   **C** on a hot, dry day.

   **D** after a volcanic eruption.

# What Are Slow Surface Changes?

Moving water can make rocks tumble and bump against each other. The rocks bump over and over again. The rocks wear down. Sharp edges become smooth and the rocks get smaller. This is an example of weathering.

Weathering is the slow wearing away of rock into smaller pieces. Moving water, ice, plant roots, and chemicals are causes of weathering.

Most rocks have tiny cracks in them. In places where it gets cold, water can get in the cracks and freeze. Ice makes the cracks bigger. Periods of freezing and melting can cause rocks to break.

The same kind of thing happens when plant roots grow into cracks in a rock. The growing roots push open the cracks. After some time the rock breaks.

## Erosion

You know that weathering is the slow wearing away of rock into smaller pieces. Erosion carries away the small pieces of rock. Erosion is the movement of rock material from one place to another.

Water is the main cause of erosion. When water flows over soil, it picks up tiny pieces of the soil. When the water moves downhill, it carries the tiny pieces with it.

Erosion of rock takes a very long time. First, the water of a fast-moving river cuts a dip into the rock. Then the running water carries away more and more material. Over a great many years, a deep canyon forms.

Wind is another cause of erosion. In some places, there are few plants. Plants are needed to hold soil in place. Without plants, the wind easily picks up dry soil.

Erosion is also caused by glaciers. A glacier is a large sheet of slow-moving ice. As it moves, a glacier can dig out huge areas of rock and soil. A glacier can dig out a valley or a canyon.

## Deposition

Erosion moves bits of sand, soil, and rock. Where do these bits go? Remember that these bits are called sediment. The dropping of sediment after it is moved is called deposition. There are three main causes of deposition—wind, glaciers, and moving water.

The wind picks up and carries dry sand. When the wind stops, the sand drops. Sand dunes are made by wind and deposition. As glaciers move, they carry rocks and soil. A melting glacier drops the rocks and soil.

Oceans and rivers also cause deposition. Ocean waves wear away some beaches. New beaches are made through deposition. Rivers slow down as they flow into a lake or ocean. Sediment settles when the moving water slows. The sediment can build up at the mouth of the river. This makes a landform called a delta.

## Mountain Building

Mountains form in different ways. A volcano can make a mountain very quickly. Other mountains form as parts of Earth's crust move. This happens slowly, over millions of years.

Sometimes huge parts of Earth's crust crash together. The crust gets pushed up and folded. The Himalayas are folded mountains. Some mountains form along a fault. Parts of Earth's crust move upward along the fault. The Sierra Nevadas in California and Nevada are fault-block mountains.

Mountains may form without folding or faulting. Pressure simply pushes up Earth's crust. The Adirondack Mountains in New York were made this way.

# What Are Slow Surface Changes?

**Use the diagram below to answer the question.**

| Date | Sand Deposit Depth at Cliff Base |
|------|----------------------------------|
| 1970 | 2.5 cm (1 in.) |
| 1975 | 5.0 cm (2 in.) |
| 1980 | 10.0 cm (4 in.) |
| 1985 | 12.5 cm (5 in.) |
| 1990 | 15.0 cm (6 in.) |
| 1995 | 20.0 cm (8 in.) |
| 2000 | 25.0 cm (10 in.) |

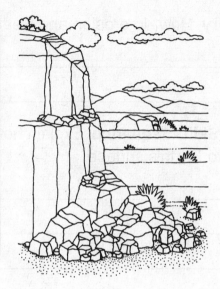

1. Describe what is happening to the cliff.

   _____

   _____

**Fill in the blanks.**

2. Water is the main cause of _____.

3. Wind, glaciers, and moving water are the main causes of

   _____.

4. When huge sections of Earth's crust collide, the crust gets pushed up and forms

   _____.

5. Some mountains form when sections of Earth's crust move upward along

   _____.

6. Mountains may also form when _____ pushes up
   Earth's crust without folding or faulting.

**7. Main Idea** What three processes slowly change Earth's surface?

_____

_____

**8. Vocabulary** How do erosion and weathering differ?

_____

_____

**9. Reading Skill: Sequence** Explain how weathering, erosion, and deposition cause changes to Earth's surface.

_____

_____

_____

**10. Critical Thinking: Apply** Give an example of erosion or deposition that you have observed in your neighborhood.

_____

_____

**11. Inquiry Skill: Infer** You notice deep grooves on a hillside building site. Soil and gravel have been washed across the road. What can you infer has happened?

_____

_____

_____

**12. Test Prep** Ocean waves change beaches through

   **A** chemical weathering.

   **B** volcanic eruptions.

   **C** erosion and deposition.

   **D** movement of Earth's crust.

# What Are Renewable Resources?

A natural resource is a material found on Earth that can be used by people. Trees, soil, and minerals are a few natural resources. Some natural resources, such as oil are nonrenewable.

A nonrenewable resource is one that cannot be replaced once it is used up or that takes thousands of years to be replaced.

A renewable resource is a natural resource that can be replaced or can replace or renew itself. Air and water are renewable resources that all living things need.

## Plants and Animals

Plants and animals are renewable resources. Animals get energy by eating plants or by eating other animals that eat plants.

Plants help clean and renew the air. Plants make their own food. As they do this, they take in a gas called carbon dioxide. They also let go of a gas called oxygen. Animals breathe oxygen from the air. Without plants, the animals would use up all the oxygen.

When old plants die, new plants often grow in their place naturally. People can help new plants grow by farming. After a food crop is picked, a new crop can be planted.

Core Skills Science, G4 SV 9781419098444

## Water as a Resource

All living things need water to live. But most of Earth's water is found in oceans. Most plants and animals cannot use this water. It has too much salt in it.

Only a small amount of Earth's water is fresh water. Most of the fresh water is under the ground or is trapped in glaciers and ice caps. Less than 1 percent of Earth's water is found in rivers and lakes. It is this water that is used for drinking and washing.

The water cycle is the way nature renews the supply of fresh water. In this cycle, energy from the Sun heats Earth's water. The heat changes the water into a gas called water vapor. The process in which liquid water changes to water vapor is called evaporation. When water evaporates, anything that is mixed with the water is left behind.

When water vapor cools it forms tiny drops of liquid water. Condensation is the process in which water vapor turns back into liquid water. This happens when water vapor rises to the upper parts of air. Air is colder higher up than it is near land.

Clouds are made when drops of water form around small particles in the air. When the drops become too heavy, they fall from the clouds as rain, snow, sleet, or hail.

Water that falls to Earth is called precipitation. Precipitation returns fresh water to Earth. Some of it flows into the ground. The rest of it flows into oceans, lakes, and rivers. The water cycle repeats again and again.

## Soil and Nutrients

Soil is an important resource. Most plants need soil to grow. Soil gives the plants support and nutrients. If the soil used for growing crops is well cared for, it can be used again and again.

Some crops use a lot of nutrients as they grow. If a farmer plants the same crop in the same soil every year, it uses up some of the nutrients. Some crops help put nutrients back into the soil. Many farmers change the crops as they grow. One time they will grow a crop that uses up nutrients. The next time they will grow a crop that gives back those nutrients.

Name _____  Date _____

# What Are Renewable Resources?

**Fill in the blanks in the diagram below.**

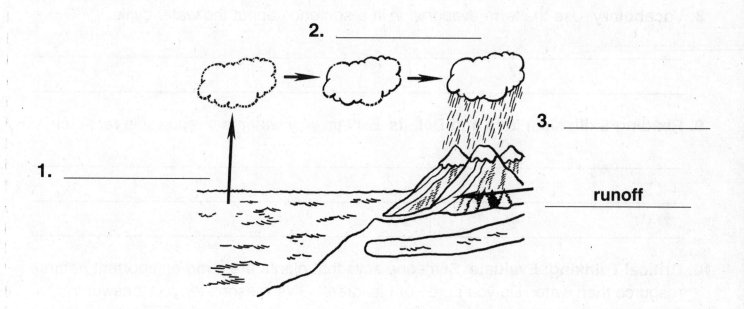

2. _____

3. _____

1. _____

runoff

**Write answers to the questions on the lines below.**

**4.** How do plants help clean and renew air?

_____

_____

**5.** What is the water cycle?

_____

_____

**6.** Why do some farmers rotate their crops?

_____

_____

_____

**7. Main Idea** What is a renewable resource?

_____

_____

**8. Vocabulary** Use the term *evaporation* in a sentence about the water cycle.

_____

_____

**9. Reading Skill: Main Idea and Details** Explain why water is a renewable resource.

_____

_____

_____

**10. Critical Thinking: Evaluate** Someone says that plants are a more important natural resource than water. Do you agree or disagree? Give reasons for your answer.

_____

_____

_____

**11. Test Prep** One example of a natural resource that is renewable is

    **A** oil.

    **B** coal.

    **C** fresh water.

    **D** gold.

# What Are Nonrenewable Resources?

People use energy every day. A small amount of energy comes from renewable resources. These resources include the Sun, wind, moving water, and heat from inside Earth.

However, most of the energy used in the United States comes from nonrenewable resources called fossil fuels. A fossil fuel is made from the remains of ancient plants and animals. Fossil fuels are oil, natural gas, and coal. These fuels began forming on Earth more than 300 million years ago.

## Coal

Coal is the most common fossil fuel on Earth. The energy stored in coal is used mainly to make electricity. It is also used for heating.

## Oil and Natural Gas

Oil and natural gas are also fossil fuels. They are formed much like coal. But instead of swamp plants, they are made from animals and plants that lived in Earth's oceans. Over millions of years, heat and pressure changed the remains of these plants and animals into oil and natural gas.

Oil is used as fuel for cars and trucks. It is also used to make things like plastics, medicines, and cloth. Natural gas is used to heat many homes and businesses. It is also used to run some machines, such as stoves.

**Oil is used to make gas, motor oil,
and asphalt for roads.**

## Fossil Fuels—Pro and Con

As sources of energy, there are some good things about fossil fuels. They are fairly easy to get out of the ground. They are easy to move from place to place. They are often cheaper than other forms of energy. There are enough supplies now to meet people's needs.

There are also some problems with using fossil fuels. All fossil fuels are nonrenewable. Some scientists think that at the rate oil and natural gas are used today, supplies may run out in 100 years. Also, using fossil fuels makes pollution. Pollution is the adding of harmful materials to the air, water, and soil. Burning fossil fuels causes air pollution.

Renewable energy sources will not run out and they do not produce pollution. But they can cost a lot. Scientists are working to find ways to make renewable energy sources cheaper and easier to use. The first car you own might run on water!

## Layers of Soil

Soil is made up in part of tiny pieces of rock. The process of making soil takes a long time. In fact, the top inch of soil in most places started forming about 500 years ago.

Nutrients lost from soil can be replaced. This means soil can be thought of as a renewable resource. But some soil is lost because of erosion. When this happens, it takes a long time to be replaced. That is why soil can be thought of as nonrenewable.

## Rocks and Minerals

Everything on Earth that is not living or has never lived is made from minerals. Living things need minerals to grow and stay healthy. Remember that rock is a solid material that is made up of one or more minerals. Rocks are always changing very slowly in the rock cycle. People mine minerals, such as iron and copper. Over time, these minerals will be replaced in the rock cycle. But the rock cycle is very slow. Plus, some minerals are rare, which means there are not a lot of them. That is why minerals are thought of as nonrenewable resources.

# What Are Nonrenewable Resources?

**Write answers to the questions on the lines below.**

**1.** What are fossil fuels?

_____

_____

**2.** How is coal used?

_____

_____

**3.** How were oil and natural gas formed?

_____

_____

_____

**4.** What are some of the benefits of using fossil fuels?

_____

_____

**5.** What are some drawbacks to using fossil fuels?

_____

_____

**6.** Why can rich soil be considered a nonrenewable resource?

_____

_____

**7. Main Idea** Why are minerals nonrenewable resources?

_____

_____

**8. Vocabulary** Explain the difference between oil and coal.

_____

_____

**9. Reading Skill: Compare and Contrast** Compare solar power and natural gas. Explain the advantages and disadvantages of each.

_____

_____

_____

**10. Critical Thinking: Predict** What might happen when oil and natural gas run out?

_____

_____

_____

**11. Inquiry Skill: Hypothesize** What would happen if an area had increased erosion?

_____

_____

_____

**12. Test Prep** Which is a nonrenewable resource?

   **A** plants

   **B** water

   **C** soil

   **D** sunlight

# What Is Air?

Did you ever wonder what is in the air you breathe? Air is made up of gases that have no color or smell. Air is all around Earth. The largest part of air is a gas called nitrogen. Plants absorb nitrogen through their roots so they can grow. The next largest part of air is a gas called oxygen. Animals need oxygen to live. Your body needs oxygen to use the fuel in the food you eat. Most living things get the oxygen they need from air.

Carbon dioxide and water are found in the air, too. Carbon dioxide is a gas that helps hold heat close to Earth. It has no color or odor. People give off carbon dioxide when they breathe. Plants use carbon dioxide to make food. When plants make food, they give off oxygen.

## Earth's Blanket

On a cold night, it is good to have a blanket. Earth has a blanket, too. It is a layer of gases called the atmosphere. The sun heats Earth. The atmosphere holds the heat close to Earth's surface.

Like all matter, air takes up space. Air also has weight. The weight of air presses down on Earth all the time. This weight is called air pressure.

High in the mountains there is less air pressing down on Earth. This means air pressure on a mountaintop is lower than it is at the bottom of the mountain.

The atmosphere has four layers. The lowest layer is called the troposphere. This layer begins at Earth's surface. Earth's weather occurs in this first layer. Weather is the conditions of the atmosphere at a certain place and time.

The next layer of the atmosphere is the stratosphere. Airplanes travel in this layer. This layer keeps a lot of the harmful part of the Sun's rays from reaching Earth.

The mesosphere is the next layer of the atmosphere. The coldest temperatures in the atmosphere are found here.

The top layer of the atmosphere is called the thermosphere. Spacecraft travel in this layer.

## Greenhouse Effect

If you have ever been in a greenhouse, you know it is warm inside. The air in a greenhouse is usually warmer than the air outside. The glass walls and roof of a greenhouse let in light and heat from the Sun. The glass traps the heat. It lets little heat out. This keeps the plants inside warm.

The atmosphere keeps Earth warm in the same way. Earth's atmosphere lets in light and heat from the Sun. Some of the heat escapes into space. But the atmosphere holds most of the heat in.

This natural heating of Earth is called the greenhouse effect. The greenhouse effect is the process by which heat from the Sun builds up near Earth's surface. The atmosphere then traps the heat there. In recent years, carbon dioxide and other harmful gases have begun to build up in the atmosphere. Some scientists warn that this build up of gases will cause Earth's air to become warmer. This is called global warming.

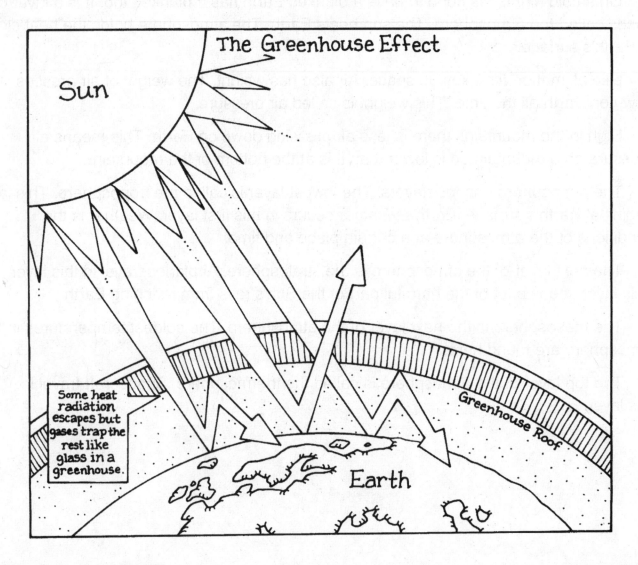

The Greenhouse Effect

Sun

Some heat radiation escapes but gases trap the rest like glass in a greenhouse.

Greenhouse Roof

Earth

Name _____   Date _____

# What Is Air?

**Write the answers to the questions on the lines.**

**1.** Write a paragraph explaining what is happening in the drawing above.

_____

_____

_____

_____

**2.** In what layer of the atmosphere are the coldest temperatures found?

_____

**3.** How do plants use nitrogen?

_____

_____

**4. Main Idea** How does the atmosphere support life on Earth?

_____

_____

**5. Vocabulary** Write a sentence using the terms *atmosphere* and *weather*.

_____

_____

**6. Reading Skill: Text Structure** Which section had the most information about the structure of the atmosphere?

_____

**7. Critical Thinking: Analyze** Trees in forests absorb carbon dioxide and store it. When trees burn, carbon dioxide is released. Carbon dioxide increases the atmosphere's greenhouse effect. What would be the long-term effect on the atmosphere if large areas of forest were burned?

_____

_____

**8. Inquiry Skill: Compare** How are the troposphere and the thermosphere different?

_____

_____

**9. Test Prep** The weight of air pressing down on an object is called

   **A** the atmosphere.

   **B** weather.

   **C** oxygen.

   **D** air pressure.

# How Does the Water Cycle Affect Weather?

Water is found in three forms, or states, on Earth. Liquid water can be seen in oceans, seas, rivers, and rain. Ice is water in its solid state. Ice forms when heat is removed from liquid water. When temperatures fall below, 0°C, liquid water becomes ice. Water in gas from is called water vapor. Water vapor is in the air, but you cannot see it. It forms when heat is added to liquid water.

When heat is added to ice, it melts. It changes to liquid water. Heat from the Sun melts ice on the lake shown below. Heat can also change liquid water to water vapor. This change is called evaporation. Evaporation happens when a liquid changes to a gas.

For example, the mist you see above a lake is not water vapor. It is a cloud of tiny drops of water. The drops formed by condensation. Condensation happens when gas changes to liquid. The water vapor came from lake water that evaporated. When the air above the lake cooled, the water vapor condensed. It became liquid again.

## The Water Cycle

The water on Earth changes from one form to another over and over again. This is called the water cycle. The water cycle is the movement of water into the air as water vapor and back to Earth's surface as precipitation. Precipitation is any form of water that falls from clouds to Earth.

Water in oceans, lakes, and rivers evaporates and becomes water vapor. As water vapor rises in the air, it cools and condenses into water droplets. These droplets form clouds. As more water vapor condenses, the drops become heavier and heavier. They become so heavy, they fall to Earth as precipitation.

Some precipitation flows downhill on Earth's surface. This water is called runoff. Runoff water flows toward streams, rivers, lakes, and oceans. Some precipitation flows down into the ground. This water is called groundwater.

## Types of Clouds

Clouds form when water vapor in the air condenses. A cloud that forms close to the ground is called fog.

**Stratus** clouds are low-level clouds that form in layers. Stratus clouds usually bring rain.

**Cumulus** clouds are fluffy and are flat at the bottom. They form low in the sky. They usually mean fair weather.

**Cirrus** clouds are thin clouds that look like feathers. They are made of ice crystals. They form high in the sky. Cirrus clouds mean the weather is fair.

**Cumulonimbus** clouds are tall and bring thunderstorms.

## Forms of Precipitation

Precipitation is any form of water that falls from clouds. Rain, snow, sleet, and hail are all forms of precipitation. Rain is the most common form of precipitation. It rains when drops of water fall through air that is above freezing. Sleet is rain that freezes as it falls. If the temperature near Earth's surface is below freezing, rain turns to ice before it reaches the ground.

Snow falls when the temperature in a cloud is below freezing. Water vapor in the cloud forms ice crystals. These ice crystals are called snowflakes. Hail forms when drops of rain freeze and strong winds carry them higher into a cloud. As hailstones fall again, more ice forms on them. They become larger. This can happen over and over. Finally, the hailstones are too heavy to be lifted by the wind. Then they fall to Earth.

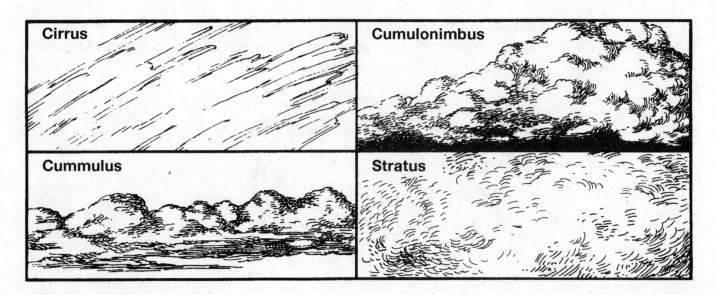

Name _____  Date _____

# How Does the Water Cycle Affect Weather?

**Answer the questions below.**

1. Based on the drawing above, what kind of cloud is it? Explain.

_____

_____

_____

2. The water on Earth _____
   over and over again as it goes through the water cycle.

3. Clouds form when _____.

4. Stratus clouds usually bring _____.

5. Precipitation is any form of _____.

6. Rain that freezes as it falls is _____.

7. _____ falls when the temperature in a cloud is below freezing.

**8. Main Idea** Describe the stages of the water cycle.

_____

_____

_____

**9. Vocabulary** What does the term *precipitation* mean?

_____

_____

**10. Reading Skill: Sequence** During a storm, rain falls to Earth's surface. The water runs into a river and out into the ocean. What happens to the water next?

_____

_____

**11. Critical Thinking: Evaluate** Suppose someone tells you that snowflakes are frozen raindrops. Is this statement true? Explain.

_____

_____

_____

**12. Inquiry Skill: Use Models** Suppose you leave a cup of water on the windowsill and the water disappears. What part of the water cycle did you model?

_____

_____

**13. Test Prep** Tall clouds that produce thunderstorms are called

   **A** cirrus.

   **B** cumulonimbus.

   **C** stratus.

   **D** cumulus.

# What Causes Weather?

Weather is all the conditions of the atmosphere at a certain time and place. These conditions include temperature, amount of water vapor in the air, wind, and air pressure.

The temperature is how hot or cold the air is. The amount of water vapor in the air is called humidity. High humidity can make the air feel wet and sticky. Wind is the movement of air. Air pressure is the weight of air as it presses down on Earth.

## Wind

Wind is moving air. Air flows from places of high pressure to places of low pressure. During the day, Earth's surfaces take in heat from the Sun. The land becomes warm quickly. It warms the air above it. As the air warms, it rises. This causes a spot of low pressure.

Oceans warm slowly. During the day, air above the ocean is not as warm as air over land. This cooler air does not rise. It stays close to Earth's surface. This causes a spot of high pressure. As the warm air above the land rises, the cooler air above the ocean moves in to take its place. This flow of air, or wind, is called a sea breeze.

## Air Masses

Each place on Earth warms or cools the air above it. This creates an air mass. An air mass is a large body of air that has about the same temperature, air pressure, and moisture.

Two conditions are used to describe air masses—temperature and humidity. Air masses are either warm or cold, and they are either moist or dry. Air masses that form in warm places are usually warm. Air masses that form near cold places are cold. Air masses that form over oceans are moist. Those over land are usually dry. Most changes in weather happen when on air mass moves into a place and pushes out another air mass.

## Weather Patterns

Air masses do not stay in one place. As they move, they bump into each other. The place where two air masses meet is called a front. A front moves across Earth's surface as one air mass pushes against the other.

The weather can change suddenly when a front moves across an area. Most storms and precipitation take place along fronts.

A cold front forms as a cold air mass meets a warm air mass. The cold air moves under the warm air, pushing it up. As the warm air rises, clouds form and precipitation occurs. Thunderstorms often happen along a cold front.

A warm front forms as a warm air mass pushes into a cold air mass. The warm air slowly moves up over the cold air. Layers of gray clouds and steady precipitation are seen when a warm front moves into an area.

## Analyzing Weather Data

A meteorologist is a scientist who studies weather. Meteorologists use measurements to identify the kinds of air masses over an area. They also predict what kind of front will form and where that front will move. This is used to create a weather map. Weather maps are often used as part of a weather forecast. A forecast is a prediction of what the weather will be for a certain day, week, or longer period of time.

## Severe Weather

Severe weather includes hurricanes, tornadoes, and snowstorms. Hurricanes often cause floods and strong winds. Severe storms, including hurricanes and blizzards, can destroy homes and put people in harm's way.

Meteorologists study storms using tools that are in space and on the ground. Forecasters give weather warnings when severe weather is likely to move into an area. These warnings can save lives.

# What Causes Weather?

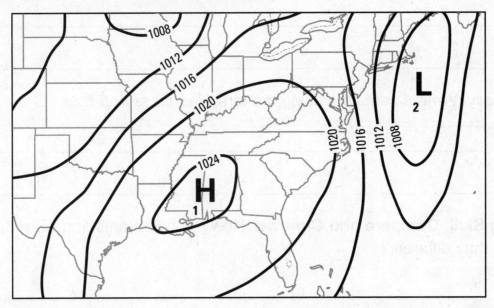

**1.** Based on the map, in what area of the United States will a front most likely occur?

_____

**2.** How does air move?

_____

**3.** When do most changes in weather occur?

_____

**4.** What is a front?

_____

**5.** What is a forecast?

_____

_____

**6.** What are three types of severe weather?

_____

7. **Main Idea** What factors are measured in weather?

_____

_____

8. **Vocabulary** Write a sentence using the terms *air mass* and *front*.

_____

_____

9. **Reading Skill: Compare and Contrast** How are cold fronts and warm fronts alike? How are they different?

_____

_____

10. **Inquiry Skill: Analyze Data** In the morning, you notice that it is warm, humid, and sunny. There is a thunderstorm in the afternoon. In the evening, it is cool and dry. What type of front passed through your area?

_____

_____

11. **Test Prep:** Which statement about warm air is NOT true?

   **A** It rises slowly.

   **B** It has lower pressure.

   **C** It forms in warm places.

   **D** It moves under cold air.

# What Are the Outer Planets?

Mercury, Venus, Earth, and Mars are the four planets closest to the Sun. They are called the inner planets. The inner planets are smaller than the other planets in the solar system. While the inner planets are made of materials that are alike, they are not exactly the same.

The four planets farthest from the Sun are the outer planets. They are very different from the inner planets. Jupiter, Saturn, Uranus, and Neptune are often called the gas giants. They are the largest planets in the solar system and are made mostly of gas.

## Jupiter

Jupiter is the largest planet. In fact, more than 1,000 Earths would fit inside Jupiter. It is so big that all the other planets would fit inside it! A huge storm in Jupiter's atmosphere, called the Great Red Spot, is more than twice the size of Earth.

Like other gas giants, Jupiter is made up mostly of gases. A very deep atmosphere that has high and low clouds covers it. These clouds change color each day. They move in bands in opposite directions. Jupiter has at least 63 moons. Scientists think the planet probably has even more moons than this.

**Sun**          **Jupiter**          **Saturn**          **Uranus**  **Neptune**

## Saturn

Saturn has bright, beautiful rings. They are made of pieces of ice, dust, and rocks. Most of these pieces are only a few centimeters (about an inch) across. Some are as large as a house. Together the rings are about 282,000 kilometers (175 miles) wide, but they are very thin.

Saturn is the second largest planet. Like the other gas giants, it is covered by clouds. It also has a small but thick rocky center. Saturn has many moons.

## Uranus

Uranus is the third largest planet. It is only one-third the size of Jupiter. As many as 64 Earths would fit into Uranus. Methane, a gas in Uranus's atmosphere, gives the planet its beautiful blue-green color.

Uranus has rings. They are very hard to see. Scientists did not even know they were there until 1977. Most were found in 1986. Uranus also has many moons. You can see Uranus in the sky with binoculars. But you have to know exactly where to look. Uranus is different from the other planets because it seems to rotate on its side.

## Neptune

Neptune is the fourth largest planet in the solar system. It is the smallest of the four gas giants. While it is a bit smaller than Uranus, Neptune has a greater mass. Neptune is almost 5 billion kilometers (about 3 billion miles) from the Sun.

Neptune has fewer moons than the other gas giants. Triton is Neptune's largest moon. Neptune has a very busy atmosphere. The winds here are very strong, and the planet has huge storms.

**Saturn has many rings.**

Name _____ Date _____

# What Are the Outer Planets?

**The outer planets below are not shown in order. Write the names of the planets on the lines below.**

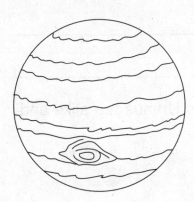

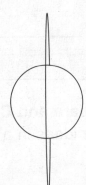

1. _____

2. _____

3. _____

4. _____

**Fill in the blanks.**

5. _____ has a beautiful blue-green color.

6. The largest planet in the solar system is _____.

7. _____ has a dense rocky center and a surface that is covered by clouds.

8. _____ is smaller and has fewer moons than the other gas giant planets.

9. **Main Idea** List the outer planets in order from nearest to farthest from the Sun.

_____

10. **Vocabulary** What is a gas giant?

_____

_____

11. **Reading Skill: Compare and Contrast** Tell how Jupiter and Uranus are alike and different. Record your ideas in a Venn diagram.

12. **Critical Thinking: Infer** What would you conclude about the temperature of the outer planets?

_____

_____

13. **Inquiry Skill: Analyze Data** Suppose you look through a pair of binoculars at night and you see a planet with rings. What planet do you see? Explain.

_____

_____

14. **Test Prep** Which is not an outer planet?

  **A** Uranus

  **B** Saturn

  **C** Venus

  **D** Neptune

# How Do Earth and Its Moon Move?

Earth makes one complete trip around the Sun in a year. While orbiting the Sun, Earth also turns on an imaginary line called an axis. With each rotation, or turn, on Earth's axis, there is one period of daylight and one period of night. Earth's axis is tilted slightly from its orbit. This tilt and Earth's orbit around the Sun cause Earth's seasons.

As Earth orbits the Sun, different parts of it are tilted toward the Sun. When the northern half of Earth tilts toward the Sun, it is summer there. Sunlight hits that part of Earth more directly. The air is warmer. The period of daylight is longer.

When the northern half of Earth tilts away from the Sun, it is winter there. Sunlight hits that part of Earth less directly. The air is colder. The period of daylight is shorter.

## How the Moon Moves

When you look at the Moon, you always see the same craters and mountains. You see the same things because the same side of the Moon always faces Earth.

Why does the same side of the Moon always face Earth? Like Earth, the Moon rotates on its axis. The Moon rotates once every 27.3 days. The Moon also orbits Earth once every 27.3 days. Because these two things take the same amount of time, the same side of the Moon always faces Earth.

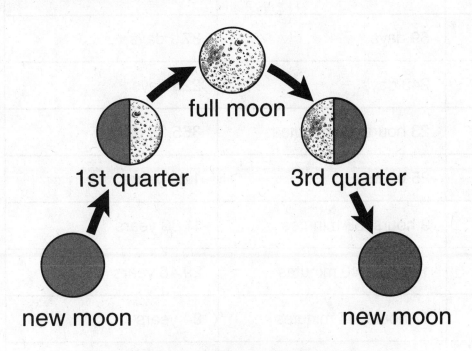

**The different ways the Moon looks are called the phases of the Moon.**

You have probably noticed that the Moon seems to change shape from one night to the next. Why? Recall that the Moon does not make its own light. It reflects, or sends back, light from the Sun.

Half of the Moon is almost always in sunlight. As the Moon orbits Earth, the amount of the lighted side facing Earth changes. These changes cause phases of the Moon. Sometimes you see just a small part of the Moon's sunlit side. This is when the Moon looks thin. Sometimes you can't see any of the Moon's sunlit side. This is called a new moon.

The Moon is not lighted by sunlight during a lunar eclipse. A lunar eclipse occurs when the Moon passes into Earth's shadow. This happens two to four times a year.

## Comparing Planet Movements

Earth rotates on its axis once each day. The other planets also rotate, but not at the same speed. The table shows how long it takes for each to rotate. All nine planets also orbit the Sun. Each revolution, or trip around the Sun, is a year. But the length of a year is different for each planet.

### Rotation and Revolution

| Planet | Period of Rotation (in Earth hours or time) | Period of Revolution |
|--------|---------------------------------------------|----------------------|
| Mercury | 59 days | 87.9 days |
| Venus | 243 days | 225 days |
| Earth | 23 hours, 56 minutes | 365.25 days |
| Mars | 25 hours | 1.88 years |
| Jupiter | 9 hours, 55 minutes | 11.86 years |
| Saturn | 10 hours 40 minutes | 29.46 years |
| Uranus | 17 hours, 14 minutes | 84 years |
| Neptune | 16 hours, 6 minutes | 164.79 years |

# How Do Earth and Its Moon Move?

**Write answers to the questions on the lines below. Use the diagram below to answer the first question.**

### Moon

| | | |
|---|---|---|
| **Temperature** | Day: 123°C (253°F)<br>Night: −233°C (−387°F) | 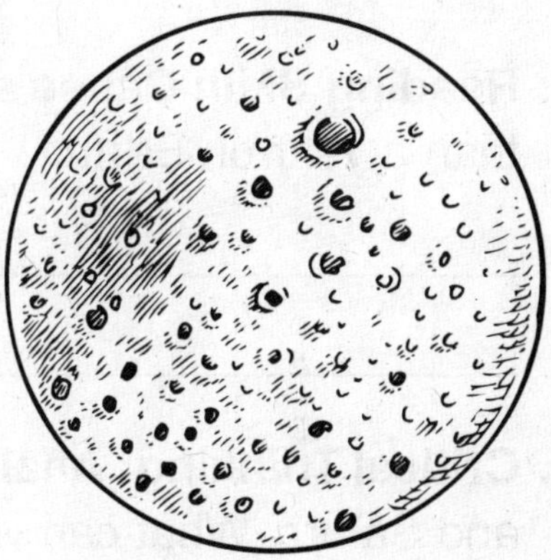 |
| **Diameter** | 3,476 km (2,085 mi) | |
| **Distance from Earth** | 384,400 km (230,600 mi) | |
| **Length of day** | About $29\frac{1}{3}$ Earth days | |

1. What can you conclude about the Moon's temperature compared to Earth's temperature?

_____

2. What are phases of the Moon?

_____

_____

3. When is the only time the Moon is not lighted by sunlight?

_____

4. Why do other planets have days that are longer or shorter than days on Earth?

_____

**5. Main Idea** The Sun shines more directly in the northern part of Earth during which season?

_____

**6. Vocabulary** Write a sentence using the term *phases of the Moon*.

_____

_____

**7. Reading Skill: Cause and Effect** Explain why a year on Neptune is much longer than a year on Earth.

_____

_____

**8. Critical Thinking: Analyze** Suppose a new planet were discovered between Jupiter and Saturn. What can you infer about the length of the new planet's year?

_____

_____

**9. Inquiry Skill: Experiment** Suppose Earth's axis became more tilted than it already is. How would this affect Earth's seasons? Make a model using a globe and a flashlight to test your ideas.

_____

_____

**10. Test Prep** The phase of the Moon when none of the lighted side is visible from Earth is called a

**A** new moon.

**B** full moon.

**C** first quarter.

**D** third quarter.

# What Are Stars and Galaxies?

A star is a huge ball of very hot gases. It gives off light, heat, and other kinds of energy. Stars can be grouped by their size, color, brightness, and temperature. Stars can shine for billions of years.

The Sun is a star. It is medium in size and brightness. Many other stars are larger and brighter. Why does the Sun look so much brighter than any other star? The reason is that the Sun is much closer to Earth than any other star. Light from the Sun takes about eight minutes to reach Earth. Light from the next closest star takes over four years to reach Earth. The Sun's energy has been giving Earth light and heat for 4.5 billion years.

## Constellations

A constellation is a group of stars that forms a pattern in the night sky. One well-known constellation is called Ursa Major, which means "Great Bear." Some of the stars in Ursa Major make up another group of stars called the Big Dipper. Another constellation looks like a lion. Another looks like a hunter. The sky is full of constellations.

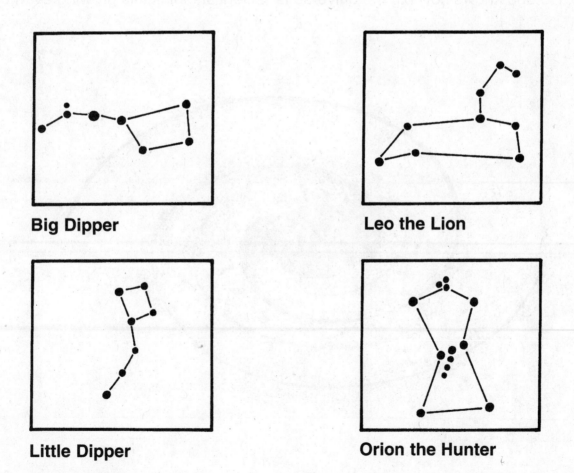

**Big Dipper**

**Leo the Lion**

**Little Dipper**

**Orion the Hunter**

Have you ever looked at a bright star early in the evening? If you look for it again later that night, it will be in a different spot. The stars do not actually move, however. They seem to move because Earth is rotating. As Earth rotates on its axis, you see different parts of the sky. The stars appear to move across the sky at night. There are stars in the sky during the day as well. The brightness of the Sun makes it impossible for you to see them.

## Galaxies

The Sun, the planets, and the moons are part of the solar system. The solar system is part of a larger group, too. It is part of a galaxy. A galaxy is a huge system, or group, of stars held together by gravity.

The solar system is in a galaxy called the Milky Way. It looks like a spiral. The stars and planets that you see at night are in the Milky Way. Not all galaxies are spiral shaped. Some galaxies are oval or round, and others are irregular.

The universe is made up of all the matter and energy there is. This includes all the galaxies and their stars, planets, and moons. There are billions of galaxies in the universe. No one knows how big the universe is. Scientists think it is growing even bigger.

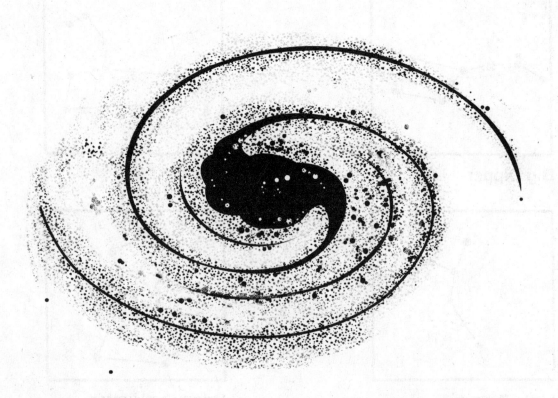

Name _____ Date _____

# What Are Stars and Galaxies?

**Fill in the blanks.**

1. Four ways that stars can be classified are _____
_____.

2. The Sun appears brighter and larger than other stars because it
_____.

3. The Sun is a star that is medium both in its _____ and its
_____.

4. The Big Dipper is a _____.

5. Stars appear to move because _____.

6. The brightness of stars makes it impossible to _____
_____.

7. A galaxy is _____
_____.

8. The Milky Way is _____
_____.

9. There are billions of galaxies in the_____.

**10. Main Idea** What objects can be found in a galaxy?

_____

_____

_____

**11. Vocabulary** Write a sentence about the universe. Be sure to use the terms *galaxy* and *stars*.

_____

_____

**12. Critical Thinking: Analyze** Suppose the Sun were bigger and brighter. What would happen to Earth?

_____

**13. Inquiry Skill: Observe** Choose a picture from this lesson. Study the picture carefully. Write a detailed description of what you see.

_____

_____

_____

_____

**14. Test Prep** A constellation is a

**A** young, growing star.

**B** ball of extremely hot gases that gives off energy.

**C** group, or system, of stars held together by gravity.

**D** group of stars that forms a pattern in the night sky.

# What Makes Up Matter?

When you look around, you may see things like cars and people. You may feel things you cannot see, like air blowing across your face. Desks, people, and blowing air are examples of matter. Matter is anything that has mass and takes up space.

Properties are special qualities for which something is known. Matter had many different properties, such as color, size, shape, and the way it feels. It is easy to see some properties of matter. You may need to use a microscope or hand lens to see other properties.

Using powerful microscopes, scientists have learned that all matter is made up of very tiny pieces called particles. The particles are always moving.

The smallest particle of matter that has the same properties of that matter is called an atom. All objects are made up of many, many atoms. In fact, there are billions of atoms in a tiny piece of sand!

Most matter is made up of atoms that have joined with other atoms to make a molecule. A molecule is one particle of matter that is made up of two or more atoms joined together. A particle of water is a molecule made up of three atoms.

## Three States of Matter

Matter comes in different forms, or states. The states of matter are three forms that matter usually takes: solid, liquid, and gas.

Water looks very different in its three states of matter. Ice is a solid. Water in a pool is a liquid. Water vapor is a gas, which you cannot see. The three states of water look different, but they are all the same kind of matter. Each particle of ice, water, and water vapor is made up of the same kind of molecule. Each molecule is made up of the same three kinds of atoms.

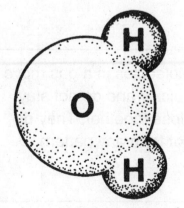

**Two hydrogen atoms and one oxygen atom combine to make a watrer molecule.**

Why do solids, liquids, and gases have different properties? The particles of matter in each of these states are put together in different ways. Look at the chart to understand how.

## Properties of Solids, Liquids, and Gases

How do you know that water is inside a boiling tea kettle? The steam you see coming from the spout is a clue. Water turns to steam. Matter can change from one state to another, but it does not become a new kind of matter. The state of matter is a physical property of matter. A physical property of matter can be seen without changing matter into something new. Size, shape, color, and the way something feels are other physical properties of matter.

Remember this about the shapes of different states of matter: A solid always keeps its own shape. A liquid takes the shape of the container it is in. A gas spreads apart or can be squeezed together to fit into spaces.

### States of Matter: Water

| Size of Matter | Molecules | Diagram |
|---|---|---|
| **Solid** The ice frozen on the ground is a solid. | Molecules in a solid are packed close together in a regular pattern. | |
| **Liquid** The water in a lake is a liquid. | Molecules in a liquid slide past each other but stay close together. They do not form a regular pattern. | |
| **Water vapor** The water vapor in the air is gas. | Molecules in a gas move quickly and do not stay close together. They do not form any pattern. | |

Name _____  Date _____

# What Makes Up Matter?

**Use the words in the box to fill in the chart.**

| oxygen | juice | carbon dioxide |
|--------|-------|----------------|
| tea | cotton | paper |
| water vapor | vinegar | steel |

| Solid | Liquid | Gas |
|-------|--------|-----|
| 1. | 4. | 7. |
| 2. | 5. | 8. |
| 3. | 6. | 9. |

**Write answers to the questions on the lines below.**

**10.** What is most matter made up of?

_____

_____

**11.** How are ice, water, and water vapor alike?

_____

_____

**12.** What are the four physical properties of matter?

_____

_____

Core Skills Science, G4 SV 9781419098444

**13. Main Idea** Explain why the color blue and the number 12 are not considered matter.

_____

_____

_____

**14. Vocabulary** What is the difference between an atom and a molecule?

_____

_____

**15. Reading Skill: Main Idea and Details** List two details that support the idea that matter has properties that can be observed.

_____

_____

_____

**16. Critical Thinking: Apply** Explain why people use solids and not liquids or gases to build houses.

_____

_____

_____

**17. Test Prep** The particles of a gas

    **A** are arranged in a pattern.

    **B** are spread far apart.

    **C** are very close together.

    **D** never move.

# How Is Matter Measured?

The metric system is a system of measurement that uses multiples of 10. Millimeters, centimeters, meters, and kilometers are used to measure length. You can change—or convert—to different metric units simply by multiplying or dividing by a multiple of 10. The metric system allows scientists to be able to communicate observations about matter.

To measure objects, people use tools that measure in metric units such as centimeters, liters, or kilograms. Length or height can be measured with a ruler that shows centimeters or meters. Mass can be measured using a balance that shows grams or kilograms. The volume of liquids can be measured with a container that shows milliliters or liters.

## Mass

Think about holding two balls, one in each hand. They are the same size, color, and shape. However, one ball feels heavier than the other. To find the difference between the balls, you can measure their masses. Mass is the amount of matter in an object. The ball that feels heavier has more mass—and more matter.

Knowing the masses of different objects helps people understand them and sort them into groups. You can use a tool called a balance to measure mass.

To measure the mass of a ball, you put it on one pan of a balance. Then you add objects called standards to the other pan. Standards are objects with known masses. As you add standards to the other pan, you watch to see when the two pans balance. When the pans balance, the total mass of the standards is the same as the mass of the ball.

## Volume

Another physical property of matter that can be measured is volume. Volume is the amount of space that matter takes up. All matter—even air and tiny particles—has mass and volume. Volume can be measured in different ways. To find the volume of a liquid, you use a measurement container such as a beaker. The volume of a liquid is measured in the metric units liters (L) and milliliters (ml).

To find the volume of a rectangular solid, such as a block, you multiply the length, width, and height of the block. The volume of a solid is measured in cubic centimeters ($cm^3$).

How do you measure the volume of a solid with a strange shape, such as a rock. First, you put some water in a beaker and write down the volume of the liquid. Then you place the rock into the beaker. The volume of liquid will now be greater. Write down the new water volume.

The change in water volume is the same as the volume of the rock. One milliliter has the same volume as one cubic centimeter. This means that if the water volume in the beaker goes up by 50 milliliters, the volume of the rock is 50 .

## Weight

You may wonder if weight of an object is the same as its mass. No. Mass is the amount of matter in an object. Weight is the measure of the pull of gravity on an object. For example, your mass is the same everywhere you go. Your weight will change as you move to different places on Earth. This is because the amount of gravity pulling on you is different in different places.

At sea level, your weight is a little bit more than it is on the top of a high mountain. This is because the pull of gravity is stronger at sea level than it is on the top of a mountain. When you move to the top of a mountain, you are farther from the center of Earth.

On the Moon, the pull of gravity is very weak. You would weigh much less on the Moon than anywhere on Earth.

# How Is Matter Measured?

**Fill in the blanks.**

1. All scientists use the _____, which is based on multiples of 10.

2. _____ is an important physical property used to identify, sort, and describe objects.

3. The amount of space matter takes up, or _____, is measured in different ways for different objects.

4. _____ is a measure of the pull of gravity on an object.

**Use the following table to answer the questions below.**

| Airport | City | State | Elevation (above sea level) |
|---------|------|-------|------------------------------|
| Denver International | Denver | Colorado | 5371 ft. |
| La Guardia | New York | New York | 10 ft. |
| Los Angeles International | Los Angeles | California | 115 ft. |
| New Orleans International | New Orleans | Louisiana | −3 ft. |
| O'Hare International | Chicago | Illinois | 659 ft. |

5. Where would a person weigh the least—Denver International or Ohare International?

_____

6. Where would the person have the least amount of mass?

_____

_____

7. Where would a person weight the most—Laguardia or New Orleans International?

_____

**8. Main Idea** What units would a scientist most likely use to measure the length of a small object?

_____

**9. Vocabulary** Write a paragraph about measuring matter. Use the terms *mass* and *volume* in the paragraph.

_____

_____

_____

_____

**10. Reading Skill: Draw Conclusions** An object has a mass of 42 g on Earth. What is its mass on the Moon?

_____

_____

**11. Critical Thinking: Evaluate** What would you say to someone who said that the metric system is not important?

_____

_____

_____

**12. Inquiry Skill: Measure** Using a metric ruler, how many centimeters long is your pen or pencil?

_____

_____

**13. Test Prep** A backyard is 1,800 cm wide. How many meters wide is it?

    **A** 18,000 m

    **B** 1,800 m

    **C** 180 m

    **D** 18 m

# What Are Physical Changes in Matter?

Suppose you are playing soccer with your friends. You kick the ball and it cracks a window of your house. The glass breaks into hundreds of tiny pieces. Your soccer ball has caused a physical change in the window glass. A physical change changes the way matter looks. It does not change it into a new kind of matter.

Many physical changes change the size, shape, or state of matter. The shape and size of the window glass changed when it broke, but each piece of broken glass still had the properties of glass. No new kinds of matter were formed.

Think about a melting juice bar. The melted part looks different from the frozen part. If you tasted the melted part of the juice bar, it would taste the same as the frozen part. The melted juice bar is not a new kind of matter. It still tastes like a frozen juice bar. It has just changed from a solid to a liquid. This change in state is a physical change.

If you hit the juice bar with a hammer, how would it change? The juice bar would probably break into smaller pieces. The smaller pieces might melt, but new kinds of matter would not be formed.

## Common Physical Changes

Suppose you are making an art project. You have cut and drawn on the paper. You have shaped the clay. You know that these changes are physical changes. They are physical changes because the paper and clay have not been changed into something new.

When matter is moved or changed, energy is at work. Energy is the ability to cause change. Sometimes energy must be added to matter to make it change. For example, heat must be added to ice so the ice will melt. Heat is a form of energy. Heat is added to a glue stick in a hot glue gun. The glue stick melts when heat is added.

Sometimes matter gives off energy when it changes. If you bend a metal paper clip back and forth many times, the clip will begin to feel warmer. That is because heat energy is given off as you bend it.

Think about physical changes that happen every day. Ice melts. Glass breaks. You cut some paper. These changes in form, size, and shape need energy. Heat energy from the Sun melts the ice. The energy of a moving soccer ball breaks the glass. The energy in your body helps you cut out a snowflake.

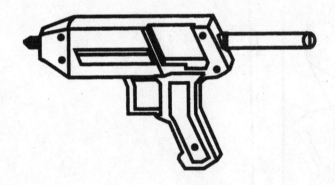

**Energy in the form of heat is added to melt the glue stick in a hot glue gun.**

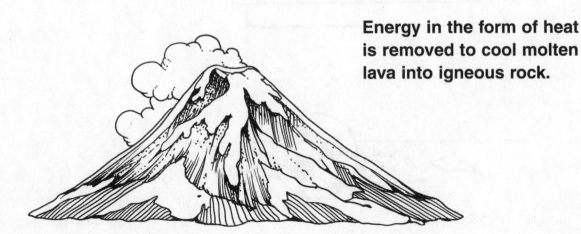

**Energy in the form of heat is removed to cool molten lava into igneous rock.**

Name _____ Date _____

# What Are Physical Changes in Matter?

**Write** *true* **if the statement is true and** *false* **if the statement is false. If the statement is false, rewrite the italicized part to make it true.**

_____ 1. Physical changes can change the *size, shape, or state* of matter.

_____

_____ 2. When a juice bar melts, *a new kind of matter* is formed.

_____

_____ 3. Whenever *matter is moved or changed,* energy is involved.

_____

_____ 4. When a paper clip is bent, *heat energy is added.*

_____

**Complete the web diagram about physical changes.**

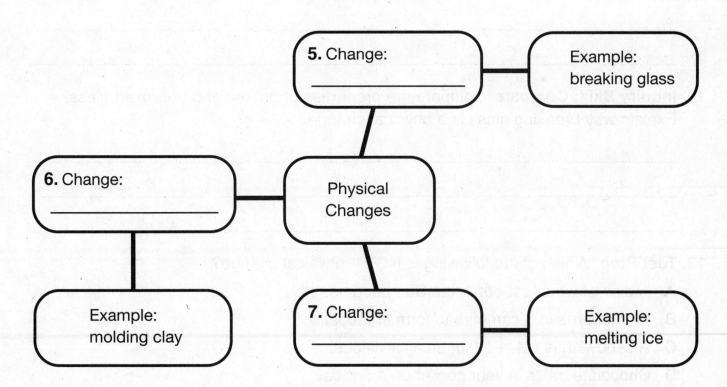

5. Change: _____

Example: breaking glass

6. Change: _____

Physical Changes

Example: molding clay

7. Change: _____

Example: melting ice

**8. Main Idea** How do you know that melting ice is a physical change?

_____

_____

**9. Vocabulary** Use your own words to describe what energy is.

_____

_____

**10. Reading Skill: Cause and Effect** What type of energy causes a rain puddle to disappear on a sunny day?

_____

**11. Critical Thinking: Analyze** A plumber uses a torch to heat a copper pipe in order to bend it. Is this change a physical change? Explain.

_____

_____

_____

**12. Inquiry Skill: Compare** Compare the properties of broken and unbroken glass. Explain why breaking glass is a physical change.

_____

_____

_____

**13. Test Prep** Which of the following is NOT a physical change?

  **A** A dish of water set out in the Sun becomes dry.

  **B** Wood burns in a campfire to form charcoal.

  **C** A sandwich is cut into four smaller pieces.

  **D** Chocolate melts in your pocket on a hot day.

# What Happens When Matter is Heated or Cooled?

Thermal energy is the total energy of the particles of matter. It has to do with the energy of moving particles. The particles of a solid have very little energy of motion. If you add more energy to particles of matter, they will move faster and farther apart.

Thermal energy can be added and taken away from matter. You cannot see thermal energy, but you can feel it as heat. Heat is the flow of thermal energy from a warmer area to a cooler area.

When you heat matter, its thermal energy grows. The particles of matter move faster and farther apart. When you cool matter, you take away thermal energy. The particles of matter slow down and move closer together.

## Temperature

Temperature is used to measure how hot or cold matter is. Temperature also tells how fast the particles of matter are moving. Particles of matter move more slowly in cold temperatures and faster in warm temperatures.

A thermometer is a tool that measures temperature. Thermometers measure temperature in units called degrees. Scientists and people in some countries use the Celsius scale of degrees. In the United States, temperature is measured using the Fahrenheit scale.

When you add heat to an object, its temperature will go up. To lower the temperature of an object, you must put it in a cooler place.

## Changes in State

The temperature of matter makes it solid, liquid, or gas. When matter is heated or cooled, its temperature changes, and it changes state. Melting, freezing, boiling, and condensation are physical changes in the state of matter.

When you heat a solid, its particles move faster and faster until they break out of their places. This change in state is melting—a solid becoming a liquid.

Particles in a liquid can move past each other, but they stay close together. When you heat a liquid its particles move faster and faster until they spread even farther apart. The liquid becomes a gas during a change in state called evaporation. Particles in a gas move quickly and there is much space between them. At very high temperatures, liquid evaporates quickly. Boiling is very fast evaporation.

If you take heat away from matter, it will change in state again. The particles of matter will move more slowly and closer together. As matter cools, gases turn into liquids—or condense. Liquids can also turn into solids—or freeze.

Changes in state are physical changes. The matter looks different because the particles of matter are in different places. The particles have not changed. The particles of ice are the same as the particles of liquid water. They are just packed together in different ways. Particles that are held together more strongly, such as in solids, need more energy to break them apart.

## Matter Stays the Same

Matter might look different after a physical change, but the kind of matter itself does not change. Is particles have not changed. They are just packed together differently.

After a physical change, the matter's physical properties, such as color and density, stay the same. Its mass, or amount of matter, also stays the same. Water is not the only kind of matter that changes state. Metals, such as iron, can also change state. When iron is heated, it gets soft. Soft metals can be hammered and bent into different shapes. When you add more heat, the metal gets softer and softer. Finally, it melts into a liquid. It has changed state, but its physical properties are still the same. It is not a new kind of matter.

Name _____ Date _____

# What Happens When Matter Is Heated or Cooled?

**Match the statement with the letter of the correct answer.**

_____ **1.** the total energy of particles in matter

_____ **2.** the flow of thermal energy from a warmer area to a cooler area

_____ **3.** the measure of how hot or cold matter is

**a.** heat

**b.** temperature

**c.** thermal energy

**Complete the chart to decribe how matter changes state.**

| State of matter | Change | Resulting state of matter |
|---|---|---|
| solid | **4.** _____ | **5.** _____ |
| liquid | **6.** _____ | solid |
| **7.** _____ | **8.** _____ | gas |

Name _____ Date _____

**9. Main Idea** How does heating affect particles of matter?

_____

_____

**10. Vocabulary** How is thermal energy related to heat?

_____

_____

**11. Reading Skill: Classify** Classify each of the following changes according to whether they are caused by adding heat or removing heat: boiling, condensation, melting, freezing.

_____

_____

**12. Critical Thinking: Apply** Which do you think would boil sooner when heated—a cup of cold water or a cup of warm water? Explain your answer.

_____

_____

**13. Inquiry Skill: Measure** What tool would you use to measure the outside air temperature?

_____

**14. Test Prep** Which occurs when heat is removed from an object?

    **A** The particles of the object move faster and farther apart.

    **B** The object expands.

    **C** The particles of the object gain thermal energy.

    **D** The particles of the object move slower and closer together.

# What Are Mixtures and Solutions?

A mixture is matter made up of two or more substances that are combined. Making a mixture is a physical change. The substances are all mixed up, but their physical properties have not changed. When substances in a mixture are very different, it is easier to separate them. Separating the parts of a mixture is a physical change.

You cannot separate all mixtures by hand. Some mixtures can be separated using a change in state. To separate a mixture of sugar and water, you could boil it. The water would change to a gas, or evaporate, and only the sugar would be left.

Different densities can also be used to separate a mixture. Density is a physical property of matter, like mass and volume. Soil could be separated into its parts by mixing it with water and letting the mixture rest. The most dense soil parts, like stones, would sink first. The less dense soil parts, like sand or clay, would sink later.

## Some Common Mixtures

There are mixtures everywhere. Bubbles are a mixture of soap and water. A bowl of soup is a mixture. Your sock drawer holds a mixture of socks. Mixtures can be any combination of matter. Some mixtures are solids, liquids, and gases together. Other mixtures have just solids, liquids, or gases.

In mixtures like vegetable soup, it is easy to see the separate parts. You can see carrots in some places and celery in other places. You can see that the substances in soup still have their physical properties.

In other mixtures, you cannot see the separate parts. In lemonade, you cannot see the water, lemon juice, and sugar that make up the mixture. These separate parts cannot be seen, but they still have their own physical properties.

**Soups and sandwiches are mixtures.**

**Physical Science**
Core Skills Science, G4 SV 9781419098444

## Solutions

A mixture of sand and water looks different from a mixture of salt and water. You can see the particles of sand in the first mixture. You cannot see the particles of salt in the second mixture. If you taste it, you know the salt is still there.

Salt water is a mixture called a solution. In a solution, the particles of one kind of matter are mixed evenly with the particles of other kinds of matter. The whole solution has the same properties.

You cannot see the salt in salt water because it has dissolved. To dissolve means to mix completely by separating into particles that you cannot see.

As salt dissolves in water, the particles of water circle around the particles of salt. The water particles and salt particles move together. After time, the solid salt is broken down into particles that are mixed evenly with water particles. When this happens, you cannot see the salt.

The properties of a solution are often different from the properties of its separate parts, but dissolving is a physical change. The physical properties of the parts of the solution stay the same.

A solution can be separated back into its parts, but not by hand. When the water evaporates from a salt water solution, the salt is left behind.

## Comparing Solutions

Some solids dissolve in water better than others. Solubility is a measure of how much of a substance can dissolve in another substance. The solubility of a substance changes in different temperatures and different substances.

Because solutions are mixtures, it does not matter exactly how much of each part is mixed together. For example, a solution of salt water can have a lot of salt and taste very salty. Or, it can have only a little salt and taste only a little salty. Both mixtures are solutions.

# What Are Mixtures and Solutions?

**Write answers to the questions on the lines below.**

**1.** What are three ways that mixtures can be separated?

_____

_____

**2.** What combinations of matter can be mixtures?

_____

_____

**3.** What is solubility?

_____

_____

**4.** What does the solubility of a substance depend upon?

_____

_____

**5.** What happens as salt dissolves in water?

_____

_____

**6.** When you add sand to water, why does the sand settle at the bottom of the water?

_____

_____

7. **Main Idea** How is a mixture made?

_____

8. **Vocabulary** What is a solution? Give an example of a solution.

_____

_____

9. **Reading Skill: Text Structure** Identify and describe the sequence of dissolving.

_____

_____

_____

_____

10. **Critical Thinking: Analyze** Why do you think it is easier to separate a mixture of two liquids with very different boiling points than two liquids with almost the same boiling points?

_____

_____

_____

11. **Inquiry Skill: Compare** Vegetable soup and tomato juice are mixtures. Describe how these mixtures are alike and different.

_____

_____

12. **Test Prep** Which of the following is a solution?

   **A** soil

   **B** rocks

   **C** lemonade

   **D** noodle soup

# How Do Light and Sound Behave?

Light is a form of energy that you can see when it interacts with matter. Light travels in waves. Waves carry energy. A high point of a wave is called a crest. A low point is called a trough. Halfway between a crest and a trough is the resting point. A wave has length and height. The length of a wave is its wavelength. The height of a wave is its amplitude.

Like water waves, light waves move in all directions from a light source. Light waves can move through matter, air, or space. Sometimes light waves cannot pass through an object. Then a shadow forms.

## Behavior of Light

When light waves hit an object, the waves can behave in four different ways. The waves can be reflected, transmitted, refracted, or absorbed. How light waves behave depends on the properties of the object they hit.

Reflection is what happens when light waves hit a surface and bounce off. When you see an object, you are really seeing light bouncing off the object.

Most surfaces reflect at least some of the light that hits them. Smooth surfaces, such as a mirror, reflect almost all the light that hits them. This makes the surface look shiny.

Some materials transmit most of the light that this them. This means the light waves pass through the materials. However, these materials may cause light to slow down and bend. The bending of light waves is called refraction. Refraction can make objects look as though they are bent or broken. Glass, water, and clear plastic can transmit and refract light.

Some materials take in, or absorb, most of the light that hits them. You cannot see light that is absorbed, because it is not reflected back to your eyes. When light waves are absorbed, the light energy changes into thermal energy, or heat. That is why objects in sunlight get hot.

## How Sounds Are Made

Sound is a form of energy made by vibrations. A vibration is a back-and-forth motion of very small pieces of matter called particles. When a material vibrates, it creates sound waves. As a sound wave moves through matter, particles are pushed together and spread apart. All sounds are made by vibrations.

Put your hand on your throat as you sing or speak. You can feel vibrations in your throat. These vibrations cause sound waves. The sound waves move through the air and into your ears. The sound waves send signals to your brain. Your brain reads those signals as sounds that are the sound of your voice.

## Properties of Sound

Sound waves are like light waves in that they have wavelength and amplitude. In a sound wave, wavelength is the distance between where particles are bunched together and where particles are spread apart. Amplitude is a measure of how close or far apart the particles are. As a sound wave moves through a material, it bunches up, spreads apart, bunches up, and spreads apart again and again. The greater the amplitude of a sound wave, the more energy it has.

A sound wave that has more energy sounds louder. The loudness of a sound is called volume. Volume depends on the amplitude of a sound wave. Volume also depends on how far the listener is from what is making the sound. This is because the amount of energy in sound waves spreads out as the waves move farther away. Also like light waves, sound waves move away from a source in all directions. Sound waves can travel through air, water, and may solid materials. However, sound waves cannot move through empty space. Sound waves must have some type of material, called a medium, to move through.

Frequency is another property of sound waves. Frequency is the number of crests and troughs produced in a certain amount of time, such as a second. The frequency of sound waves determines the pitch of the sound. Pitch is how high or low a sound seems to a listener. Sounds with a low frequency produce a low number of crests and troughs in a second. These sounds also have a low pitch. Sounds with a high frequency produce more crests and troughs. They have a high pitch.

# How Do Light and Sound Behave?

Use the diagram below to answer the question.

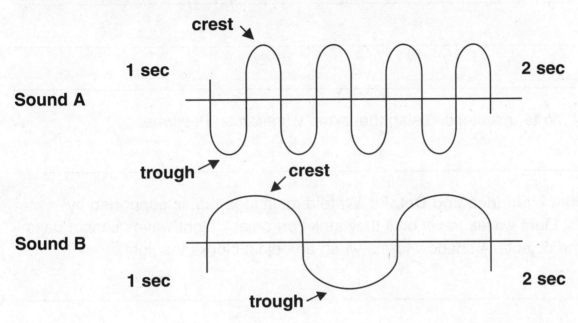

1. An ambulance siren would produce which sound wave above? Explain.

_____

_____

**Write the answers to the questions on the lines below.**

2. What is amplitude?

_____

3. What happens when light waves are absorbed?

_____

4. What is a resting point?

_____

5. What is the material through which sound travels?

_____

**6. Main Idea** What are four ways that light waves can behave when they strike an object?

_____

_____

_____

**7. Vocabulary** Write a sentence using the terms *vibration* and *volume*.

_____

**8. Reading Skill: Main Idea and Details** Write a main idea that is supported by these details: Light waves travel until they strike an object. Light waves cannot pass through some objects. A shadow forms when an object blocks the light.

_____

_____

**9. Inquiry Skill: Observe** A straight ladder in a swimming pool appears to be broken where it enters the water. What behavior of light causes this?

_____

_____

**10. Test Prep** Sound waves send signals to your

    **A** ear.

    **B** brain.

    **C** throat.

    **D** heart.

# What Is Static Electricity?

Have you ever felt a shock from a doorknob after walking on a carpet? Here's why. You know that all matter is made up of tiny particles called atoms. Doorknobs and carpet are made of atoms. Atoms are made up of even tinier particles. Many of these tiny particles carry units of electricity called electric charges. These charges gave you the shock.

There are positive electric charges and negative electric charges. Charges that are the same are called like charges. Charges that are different are called unlike charges. Most matter is electrically neutral. Electrically neutral means matter has an equal number of positive and negative charges.

## How Charges Behave

Electric charges can act on each other, even without touching. Like charges repel. They push away from each other. Unlike charges attract. They pull toward each other. Two objects with like charges push away from each other. Two objects with unlike charges pull toward each other.

Negative charges are attracted to positive charges. Particles that have a negative charge can move more easily from one material to another than particles with a positive charge can. So negative charges tend to move toward matter that is positively charged.

Negative charges do not usually move toward an electrically neutral object. However, negative charges can be made to move. Rubbing can move negative charges from one electrically neutral object to another.

## Buildup and Discharge

Sometimes an electric charge builds up on a material. This built-up electric charge is called static electricity. When you hair stands on end and moves toward a plastic comb, you can see static electricity at work.

Running a comb through your hair moves negatively charged particles from your hair onto the comb. Your hair loses negative charges and has an overall positive charge. The comb gains negative charges and now has an overall negative charge.

Your hair and the comb now have unlike charges. They attract each other. Each hair on your head now has a like charge. They repel each other. The result is they stand on end and push away from each other.

You sometimes get a shock when you touch a metal doorknob. The shock is caused by a release of electric charges. Your body has built up a negative charge. When you touch the doorknob, the charge quickly jumps from you to the doorknob. This release of the built-up negative charge is called an electric discharge, or spark.

# What Is Static Electricity?

**Write the answers to the questions on the lines below.**

1. What is an electric charge?

   _____

3. What is electrically neutral matter?

   _____

3. What is negatively charged matter?

   _____

4. How do like charges affect each other?

   _____

5. How do unlike charges affect each other?

   _____

6. What type of electrically charged particles move from one material to another more easily?

   _____

7. What causes your hair to stand on end?

   _____

8. What happens when an object with a negative charge touches another object?

   _____

**9. Main Idea** When does an object have an overall positive charge?

_____

_____

**10. Vocabulary** Write a short paragraph using the terms *static electricity* and *electric discharge*.

_____

_____

_____

**11. Reading Skill: Cause and Effect** Explain how rubbing an object with a piece of cloth could change the overall charge of the object.

_____

_____

**12. Critical Thinking: Apply** Suppose you pull a shirt from the dryer. It has a sock stuck to it. Explain why this happens.

_____

_____

**13. Inquiry Skill: Infer** Object A has a positive electric charge. Object A and Object B attract each other. What can you infer about the overall electric charge of Object B?

_____

**14. Test Prep** A built-up electric charge is

  **A** electrically neutral.

  **B** static electricity.

  **C** positively charged.

  **D** electric discharge.

# What Is Electric Current?

Charged particles can be made to move, or flow, instead of building up. The energy of these particles can be controlled and used. The constant flow of electric charges is called electric current. You can use electric current to toast a piece of bread.

## Conductors and Insulators

Negatively charged particles move easily through materials called conductors. Electric current easily passes through some metals. Metals such as copper and silver are good conductors. Water and living things are also good conductors.

Materials that electric charges do not flow through easily are called insulators. Materials such as plastic and rubber are good insulators. Conductors and insulators are used to control and direct electric flow.

## Circuits and Switches

The pathway that electric current follows is called an electric circuit. A circuit is a closed pathway. A closed pathway does not have any gaps, or openings. Another name for a closed pathway is a complete pathway.

You can make a simple circuit. You just need wire, a battery, and a light bulb. When you connect these items without gaps, you create a closed circuit. When charges flow through the closed circuit, the light bulb will light. If there is a gap, or an opening, in the circuit, it is an open circuit. A circuit with gaps is also known as an incomplete circuit. When a circuit has gaps, electric charges cannot complete the path. The light bulb will not light.

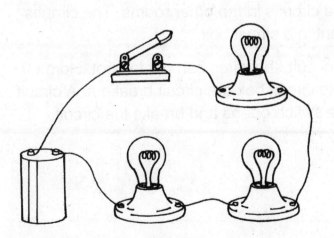

**incomplete pathway**

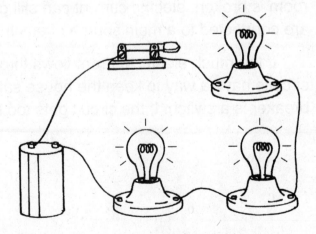

**complete pathway**

Most circuits have a switch that opens and closes the circuit. A switch lets you turn a light bulb on and off. When you flip the switch on, you close the circuit. The light bulb goes on. When you flip the switch off, you open the circuit. The light bulb goes off.

Some electrical objects are run by batteries. A battery is made up of one or more electric cells. An electric cell is an object that changes chemical energy into electrical energy. A flashlight is battery-powered. It is also an example of a simple circuit with a switch.

## Two Types of Circuits

Every working circuit has at least three parts:

· A power source, such as a battery

· A conductor, usually wire

· An object that uses electric current, such as a light bulb

But a circuit can have many parts. It can have a switch. It can have more than one object using the electric current. In a series circuit, the parts are connected in just one pathway. Electric current flows through each part. Electric current will flow through a series circuit only if all the parts are connected.

In a parallel circuit, the parts are connected in more than one pathway. Electric current can flow through all the parts in many ways. Electric current will flow through a parallel circuit even if all the parts are not connected.

## Electricity in the Home

The electric wiring in a house is connected in parallel circuits. If the circuit for one room is broken, electric current can still go to the circuits in the other rooms. The circuits are connected to a main source of electric current in a circuit box.

If too much electric current flows through a circuit, the wires can get too hot. Home circuits have a way to keep the house safe. In the circuit box are circuit breakers. A circuit breaker is a switch. If the circuit gets too hot, the switch opens and breaks the circuit.

# What Is Electric Current?

**Fill in the blanks.**

1. A continuous flow of electric charges is called an electric _____.

2. Negatively charged particles move easily through materials that are _____.

3. Materials that are _____ do not allow electric charges to flow easily through them.

4. Electric charges can move if they have a _____ pathway to follow.

**Use the drawing below to answer questions 6–7.**

**Series Circuit**

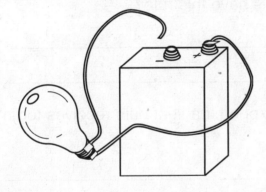

**Parallel Circuit**

5. What has happened to the series circuit? Explain.

_____

_____

6. What will happen to the parallel circuit if the top light bulb is broken? Explain.

_____

_____

**7. Main Idea** Explain why a switch might be added to a circuit. Give examples.

_____

_____

**8. Vocabulary** What is a conductor?

_____

_____

**9. Reading Skill: Compare and Contrast** Why is the wiring in a house usually connected in parallel circuits and not in series circuits?

_____

_____

**10. Critical Thinking: Analyze** At public swimming pools, swimmers are not allowed in the water during a thunderstorm. Why do pools have this rule?

_____

_____

**11. Inquiry Skill: Predict** What most likely will happen if a light bulb receives too much electricity?

_____

_____

**12. Test Prep** An electric cell is a device that

   **A** opens and closes circuits.

   **B** cannot be used in a parallel circuit.

   **C** cannot be used in a series circuit.

   **D** changes chemical energy into electrical energy.

# What Are Gravity and Friction?

You push a heavy box across a floor. You pull a wagon behind you. You use pushes and pulls to make objects change their motion. A force is a push or a pull. A push is a force that moves an object away. A pull is a force that moves an object nearer. A force can change the motion of an object. A force can start an object moving. A force can change the direction or speed of an object. A force can stop an object from moving.

Think about moving a heavy box across the floor. The box has no motion until you push it. It moves in one direction as you push it in that direction. You can change the speed of the box. You do that by using a different force. You must push the box harder to move it faster. You would also have to push harder on a box with a greater mass in order to move it.

You can change the direction of the box by using a different force. You must push the box from a different side. Or you must push the box from a different direction. You can stop the box from moving if you stop pushing it.

## Friction

When you stop pushing a heavy box, different force stops the box from sliding. That force is called friction. Friction is a force that slows or stops motion between two surfaces that touch each other.

There is more friction between rough surfaces. There is less friction between smooth surfaces. So there is some friction between a box and a smooth tile floor. There is more friction between a box and a rough concrete floor.

Friction can be useful. Without friction, you would slip and slide. Friction helps you hold pencil. Without friction, you would not be able to write. The pencil would slip out of your hand.

**There is friction between the box and the floor.**

There is even friction between objects and the air. This is called air resistance. You can feel air resistance when you ride a bicycle.

Friction slows or stops movement. This can sometimes be useful. A wheelchair stays in place because of the friction between the wheel and the brake. But sometimes less friction is better. For example, less friction between snow and a snowboard lets the snowboard go faster.

There are ways to create less friction between objects. One way is to put slippery matter on surfaces that touch. You can put slippery wax on the bottom of the snowboard. This makes less friction between a snowboard and the snow. This makes the snowboard go faster.

Wheels also reduce, or make less, friction. Wheels roll over a surface instead of sliding on it. Some machines use small rolling metal balls between their surfaces. This reduces friction between moving parts. These balls are called ball bearings.

Some moving objects are built to have less friction with air. This helps them move faster through the air. Race cars and airplanes have smooth shapes. This helps the air slide over them. Runners wear smooth, tight-fitting clothing for the same reason.

Friction is one natural force that makes objects change their motion. Friction acts on objects that are touching each other.

## Gravity

Gravity is a force that pulls objects toward each other. Earth's gravity pulls skydivers toward the ground. Gravity also keeps your books on your desk. It makes rain fall from the clouds.

Gravity can act on objects that are close or at a distance. Earth's gravity can even act on objects in space. Gravity holds the Moon in orbit around Earth. Objects with greater mass have greater gravity. Earth has more mass than the Moon. Earth's gravity is stronger than the Moon's gravity.

When people landed on the Moon, they could jump higher and lift heavier objects than they could on Earth. That is because the Moon's gravity is weaker.

Name _____ Date _____

# What Are Gravity and Friction?

**Write answers to the questions on the lines below.**

**1.** What kind of force moves an object away?

_____

**2.** In what ways can a force change the motion of an object?

_____

_____

**3.** How does friction help us move from place to place?

_____

**4.** In the drawing above, what force is acting at arrow A?

_____

**5.** In the drawing above, what force is acting at arrow B?

_____

**6.** Why do racecars and airplanes have sleek shapes?

_____

**7.** Why do objects fall to Earth?

_____

**8. Main Idea** Give two example of forces.

_____

**9. Vocabulary** What is *friction*?

_____

_____

**10. Reading Skill: Cause and Effect** Suppose you are pushing a wheelbarrow. What would be the effect if you applied a greater pushing force to the wheelbarrow?

_____

**11. Critical Thinking: Analyze** When you swing, you push your feet against the ground to start moving. When you want to stop, you drag your feet on the ground until the swing stops. Describe each force that changes your motion on the swing.

_____

_____

_____

**12. Inquiry Skill: Compare** What is the difference between a push and a pull?

_____

_____

**13. Test Prep** Which statement is true about gravity?

    **A**  It acts only on objects that are touching.

    **B**  It can act over a distance.

    **C**  It is a pushing force.

    **D**  Only very large objects have it.

# Answer Key

## Life Science
### How Are Living Things Organized?

1. mitochondria
2. chromosomes
3. nucleus
4. cell membrane
5. A
6. C
7. D
8. A
9. They are made of cells and perform life process.
10. An organ system is a group of organs that work together.
11. Both look the same. The person is living, but the model is not.
12. Sample answer: They carry out life processes and are alive.
13. Answers may vary.
14. C

### How Do Plants Carry Out Life Processes?

1. flower
2. leaf
3. stem
4. root
5. by leaf, stem, or root
6. the taproot and the fibrous root
7. the process plants use to make food
8. Roots take in water and nutrients from the soil.
9. green material that helps plants make food
10. leaves and roots
11. photosynthesis; making food.
12. sunlight
13. A

### What Is the Digestive System?

1. energy
2. growth
3. proteins
4. saliva
5. esophagus
6. stomach
7. small intestine
8. blood
9. solid waste
10. breaks down food, allows blood to absorb nutrients
11. Food stays in the large intestine from 12 to 36 hours.
12. Fats and carbohydrates in food are broken down. Protein digestion is completed.

13. flow chart sequence: mouth, esophagus, stomach, small intestine, large intestine
14. B

### What Are the Circulatory and Respiratory Systems?

1. platelets
2. carbon dioxide
3. diaphragm
4. capillary
5. blood
6. to the heart through
7. arteries
8. veins
9. respiratory system: takes in oxygen delivers to lungs; circulatory system: delivers oxygen from lungs to cells
10. Answers may vary.
11. They are both solids in the blood; red carry oxygen, white fight disease
12. Blood in the circulatory system moves in a path like a circle.
13. 10,000 mL of air
14. C

### What Are the Skeletal and Muscular Systems?

1. Ribs
2. ball-and-socket joint
3. Cartilage
4. skull
5. spine
6. hinge
7. skeletal, cardiac, and smooth
8. Skeletal muscles are voluntary. Cardiac and smooth muscles are involuntary.
9. give the body shape and support, protection, and help with movement
10. Answers may vary.
11. You would not be able to move.
12. Answers may vary.
13. C

### How Do Plant and Animal Life Cycles Vary?

1. incomplete; three stages; nymph
2. insect; birds and alligators do not undergo metamorphosis
3. embryo
4. germinate
5. larva
6. seed germination, growth into an adult, reproduction, death
7. Answers may vary.

8. It makes seeds.
9. Answers may vary.
10. Bar graphs should accurately represent data given.
11. D

### What Are the Parts of Ecosystems?

1. A
2. A
3. C
4. B
5. all the living things in an ecosystem
6. all the members of one kind of plant or animal
7. a grassy land area with few or no trees that is hot in the summer and cold in the winter
8. Animals eat plants and other animals for food. Plants depend on organic matter to enrich the soil.
9. Answers may vary.
10. Sample answer: Many animals would lose their homes.
11. Living things depend on nonliving things in the ecosystem.
12. On the forest floor, sunlight is blocked by the tall trees.
13. B

### How Does Energy Flow in a Food Web?

1. It shows the path of energy in an ecosystem.
2. bird; it eats leaves and grasshoppers
3. snake; hawk
4. mouse; grasshopper; rabbit
5. hawk; fox
6. from producers to herbivores to carnivores
7. Both show energy pathways; food chain: one energy pathway; food web: two or more food chains.
8. Food energy passes from plants to prey animals that are herbivores and omnivores.
9. Many people are omnivores—they eat plants and meat. Other people are herbivores—they eat vegetables and fruits.
10. Sample answer: grass—cow—person
11. B

# Answer Key

## How Is Matter Cycled in an Ecosystem?

1. It is recycled by the cow. It dies and is eaten by decomposers.
2. The Sun is the beginning because plants need the Sun so that they can make their food.
3. It will eventually die and decomposers will break down its body into nutrients for the soil.
4. recycling
5. scavengers and decomposers
6. Answers may vary.
7. The scavengers would not find the remains of prey animals to eat. Scavengers would not be eaten by predators, and the population would grow.
8. Nutrients would not be recycled in the ecosystem, the food supply would be reduced, and some organisms would not survive.
9. the amount of light
10. B

## How Are Organisms Adapted to Survive?

1. behavior
2. camouflage
3. mimicry
4. behavior
5. camouflage
6. behavior
7. behavior
8. An organism that is not adapted to its environment has little chance of surviving.
9. it includes the kind of food a living thing uses
10. While hibernating, a frog uses little energy and does not need to eat.
11. will have a hard time hiding
12. coloring, markings, shape of the body
13. B

## Earth Science

### What Is the Rock Cycle?

1. igneous
2. metamorphic
3. sedimentary
4. minerals
5. weathering
6. sediment
7. metamorphic
8. rock cycle
9. weathering, heat and pressure, and cooling
10. Minerals have a definite chemical makeup. Rocks can be made up of one or more minerals.
11. sedimentary rock
12. Metamorphic rocks can form when igneous rocks are subjected to heat and pressure. Igneous rocks can form from melted metamorphic rocks.
13. B

## What Are Rapid Surface Changes?

1. C
2. A
3. E
4. D
5. B
6. sections of Earth's crust
7. create landforms
8. Pressure
9. change
10. landslides and mudslides
11. earthquakes, volcanoes, landslides
12. Answers may vary.
13. It can form a mountain, a valley, or a new fault.
14. Students' models will vary.
15. C

## What Are Slow Surface Changes?

1. slow weathering and erosion
2. erosion
3. deposition
4. folded mountains
5. a fault
6. pressure
7. erosion, deposition, mountain building
8. Weathering is the breaking down of rock into smaller pieces. Erosion is the carrying away of the pieces.
9. Rock is broken down by weathering. Then the pieces are carried to another place by erosion. Finally, the pieces are dropped by deposition.
10. Answers will vary.
11. Heavy rains probably fell. The water formed small streams down the hillside and washed the soil across the street.
12. C

## What Are Renewable Resources?

1. evaporation
2. condensation
3. precipitation
4. They take in carbon-dioxide and release oxygen.
5. a natural process that renews the supply of fresh water
6. to help replace nutrients
7. a resource that can be replaced or can renew itself
8. Answers may vary.
9. The water cycle renews our supply of fresh water.
10. Answers should indicate an understanding that life on Earth would not be possible without water and plants.
11. C

## What Are Nonrenewable Resources?

1. fuel formed from the remains of ancient plants and animals
2. for heating; to make electricity
3. heat and pressure changed the remains of plants and animals
4. They are fairly easy to remove from the ground, usually cheaper than other forms of energy, and can be easily transported.
5. They are nonrenewable and produce pollution
6. Soil lost to erosion takes a very long time to replace.
7. they take a long time to replace; some are rare
8. Coal is formed from ancient swamp plants; oil is formed from ancient animals and plants that lived in Earth's oceans.
9. Solar power is renewable, does not cause pollution, and is expensive. Natural gas is nonrenewable but cheaper.
10. People will have to use alternate energy resources.
11. The amount of soil would lessen.
12. C

## What Is Air?

1. Sample answer: Factories and cars release carbon dioxide and other harmful fumes into the air. The fumes build up and become trapped in the atmosphere. This is called global warming.

# Answer Key

2. mesosphere
3. They absorb it through their roots so they can grow.
4. It blocks the Sun's harmful rays and keeps heat close to Earth.
5. Answers may vary.
6. Earth's Blanket
7. More carbon dioxide would be released, and the greenhouse effect would increase.
8. The troposphere has weather, as well as the thickest air. The thermosphere has no weather and has the thinnest air.
9. D

## How Does the Water Cycle Affect Weather?

1. cumulonimbus; stratus and cumulonimbus clouds bring rain, but stratus clouds form in layers
2. changes from one form to another
3. water vapor in the air condenses
4. steady rain
5. water that falls from clouds to Earth
6. sleet
7. snow
8. Water evaporates from bodies of water. It condenses in the air and forms clouds. The droplets in clouds grow larger until they fall back to Earth.
9. rain, snow, sleet, and hail.
10. The water evaporates into water vapor.
11. No, sleet is frozen rain. Snowflakes are ice crystals.
12. evaporation
13. B

## What Causes Weather?

1. the northeast
2. from areas of high pressure to areas of low pressure
3. when one air mass moves into an area and pushes out another air mass
4. the place where two air masses meet
5. a prediction of the weather
6. hurricanes, tornadoes, and snowstorms
7. temperature, humidity, wind, and air pressure
8. Answers may vary.
9. Alike: they move; they change weather; Different: cold fronts push warm air up and bring thunderstorms; warm fronts rise slowly and bring layers of gray clouds and steady precipitation
10. A cold front passed through the area.
11. D

## What Are the Outer Planets?

1. Jupiter
2. Uranus
3. Saturn
4. Neptune
5. Uranus
6. Jupiter
7. Saturn
8. Neptune
9. Jupiter, Saturn, Uranus, Neptune
10. largest planets in our solar system; mostly made of gas
11. Jupiter: clouds, Great Red Spot; Both: made of gases; outer planets; Uranus: blue-green, rotates on side
12. it is very cold
13. Uranus; it has rings; you can see it through binoculars
14. C

## How Do Earth and Its Moon Move?

1. temperatures are more extreme than Earth's; the Moon is much hotter and much colder
2. changes in the lighted side of the Moon that you can see from Earth
3. during a lunar eclipse
4. The planets rotate at different speeds
5. summer
6. Answers may vary.
7. Neptune is the farthest planet from the Sun, so it takes the longest time to complete one revolution.
8. Its year would be longer than Jupiter's and shorter than Saturn's.
9. Summers would be hotter with longer days. Winters would be colder with shorter days.
10. A

## What Are Stars and Galaxies?

1. by size, color, brightness, and temperature
2. is closer to Earth than other stars
3. size, brightness
4. constellation
5. Earth is rotating
6. see them during the day
7. a huge system of stars held together by gravity
8. a spiral-shaped galaxy that contains the solar system
9. universe
10. stars, planets, and moons
11. Answers may vary.
12. The temperature would increase so that all living things would die.
13. Answers will vary.
14. D

## Physical Science
## What Makes Up Matter?

1–3. any order: cotton, paper, steel
4–6. any order: tea, vinegar, bleach
7–9. any order: oxygen, carbon dioxide, water vapor
10. Most matter is made up of molecules.
11. They are all the same kind of matter.
12. size, shape, color, and texture
13. They have no mass and do not take up space.
14. An atom is the smallest particle of matter. A molecule is a combination of two or more atoms.
15. Matter has mass. Matter takes up space.
16. Materials used to build houses have a definite shape and size, so houses will be sturdy. Liquids have no shape or size and cannot hold up a building.
17. B

## How Is Matter Measured?

1. metric system
2. Mass
3. volume
4. weight
5. Denver International
6. The person's mass is always the same no matter where the person is.
7. New Orleans International
8. millimeters or centimeters
9. Answers may vary.
10. 42g
11. It allows scientists to communicate observations about matter.
12. Answers may vary.
13. D

© Houghton Mifflin Harcourt Publishing Company
Core Skills Science, G4 SV 9781419098444

# Answer Key

## What Are Physical Changes in Matter?

1. true
2. false; no new matter
3. true
4. false; heat energy is given off.
5. size
6. shape
7. state
8. No new matter was formed.
9. the ability to cause change
10. the Sun's energy
11. Yes, the matter is still copper.
12. Both are transparent, smooth, and with sharp edges. They have different sizes and shapes. The change is physical because the glass is the same kind of matter before and after.
13. B

## What Happens When Matter Is Heated or Cooled?

1. C
2. A
3. B
4. melting
5. liquid
6. freezing
7. liquid
8. evaporating
9. Heating makes particles speed up and spread out.
10. Heat is the movement of thermal energy from a warmer place to a cooler place.
11. Boiling and melting add heat. Condensation and freezing remove heat.
12. Warm water would boil sooner because it already has more thermal energy.
13. thermometer
14. D

## What Are Mixtures and Solutions?

1. by hand, a change in state, or differences in density
2. any combination
3. how much of a substance can dissolve in another substance
4. the temperature and the substance in which it is dissolving
5. The particles move together.
6. Sand is not soluble in water.
7. by physically combining two or more substances
8. a mixture in which the particles of one kind of matter are evenly mixed with the particles of other kinds of matter; salt water
9. First, one substance is mixed with another. The particles of the second substance surround and pull apart the particles of the first substance. The particles of the first substance spread evenly throughout the second substance.
10. One substance will boil away and leave the other.
11. Both are made up of 2 or more kinds of matter. The soup is not mixed evenly, while the juice is.
12. C

## How Do Light and Sound Behave?

1. A. Sirens make high-frequencies sounds.
2. how closely particles are pushed together or spread apart
3. The light energy changes into thermal energy.
4. the halfway point between a crest and a trough.
5. medium
6. reflected, transmitted, refracted, or absorbed
7. Answers may vary.
8. Answers may vary.
9. refraction
10. B

## What Is Static Electricity?

1. the units of electricity that very tiny particles of matter carry
2. matter with the same number of positive and negative charges
3. matter that has more negative than positive charges
4. Like charges repel each other.
5. Unlike charges attract each other.
6. negative
7. Negative particles from your hair move to your comb. Each hair on your heat now has a like charge so the repel each other.
8. Static electricity discharges.
9. when it has more positive than negative charges
10. Answers may vary.
11. Rubbing makes negative particles move.
12. Clothes rub together in the dryer, causing charges to move and giving them opposite charges, which attract.
13. Object B has an overall negative charge.
14. B

## What Is Electric Current?

1. current
2. conductors
3. insulators
4. complete
5. The wire is not touching the battery so the light bulb is off; it is an incomplete circuit
6. The bottom light bulb will still work because there will still be a flow of electric current.
7. to start and stop electric current
8. a material that negatively charged particles can move through easily
9. Parallel circuits include two or more paths for electricity, so a break does not stop the flow of electricity.
10. Lightning could strike the water, travel through it, and electrocute anyone in the pool.
11. The light bulb will burn out.
12. D

## What Are Gravity and Friction?

1. a push or pull
2. A force can start an object moving, change its direction or speed, or stop it from moving.
3. Without friction, we would slip and slide on every surface.
4. gravity
5. friction or pull
6. to help air slide over them
7. gravity
8. any two: a push, a pull, gravity, friction
9. Friction is a force that slows or stops motion between two surfaces that are touching.
10. the wheelbarrow would move faster.
11. You push against the ground to overcome gravity. You drag your feet on the ground to cause friction.
12. A push moves objects away from each other. A pull moves objects toward each other.
13. B